W9-CMP-968

MAN ON EARTH

By the same author

Archaeology of Jersey
Prehistoric Britain
Early Britain
Symbols and Speculations (*Poetry*)
A Land
A Guide to the Prehistoric and Roman Monuments of England and Wales
A Woman as Great as the World and Other Fables

man on earth

Jacquetta (Hopkins) Hawkes

Random House : New York

American Edition published 1955

Library of Congress Catalog Card Number: 55-5799
Manufactured in the United States of America
by H. Wolff, New York

TO JACK

contents

1 the seasons of the plain 3

2 backbone 16

The body is roughed-out

3 blood 44

The body is warmed

4 culture 57

The body is completed and culture begun

5 brain 104

The meeting-place of body and culture

6 civilization 134

The building of human worlds

7 intellect 171

The steeling of rational thought

8 a myth for the future 207

APPENDIX

Geological Time-scale 232

Man's Genealogy 233

INDEX 235

illustrations

facing page

20 THE EVOLUTION OF MAN'S SKULL

21 MAN'S BRAIN, SIDE VIEW AND SECTION

52 MAN AS HUNTER
"The ornamentation of the person comes close to the bone of human nature."

53 THE VILLAGE MAYOR: EGYPTIAN OLD KINGDOM
"Man sees himself as he is, yet loves what he sees." *(N. Y. Public Library Picture Collection)*

84 THE SCRIBES
Securing the spoken word which, until then, had drifted into oblivion *(N. Y. Public Library Picture Collection)*

85 PHARAOH AKHENATEN
The first individual in history? *(N. Y. Public Library Picture Collection)*

116 BUDDHA MEDITATING
". . . learning to control the strange, hidden world of the psyche." *(By courtesy of Metropolitan Museum of Art)*

117 CHINESE SAGE
". . . man . . . in modest harmony with nature." *(N. Y. Public Library Picture Collection)*

180 GREEK HEAD
"Man the measure of all things": idealizing humanism *(N. Y. Public Library Picture Collection)*

181 GOTHIC HEAD
". . . man . . . as a transfigured vessel for the grace of God." *(N. Y. Public Library Picture Collection)*

212 RENAISSANCE MAN IN HIS CONFIDENT PRIDE
(By courtesy of Metropolitan Museum of Art)

213 HUMAN FIGURE: HENRY MOORE
". . . our loss of confidence in ourselves . . ."

Author's note

I want to thank Dr. Kenneth Oakley for the valuable suggestions he made after reading my proofs and for allowing me to reproduce the genealogical tree on page 233, and Mr. W. Grey Walker for reading Chapter 5. I am grateful to Mr. Henry Moore for the photograph of his Human Figure.

MAN ON EARTH

the seasons of the plain 1

When I was a girl I took part in the excavation of a cave-dwelling on the lowest slopes of Mount Carmel in Palestine. The ancient inhabitants of the cave had been human beings of a kind, but human beings who differed conspicuously from ourselves both in body and mind. Indeed, this race had lived at the parting of the ways where the road leading to our own higher consciousness left the easier highway of animal vitality.

The cave lay in the last rocky fringes of the clumsy mountain mass of Carmel, and the terrace outside it, where most of our work was done, looked across the flat coastal plain towards the sea. There on the horizon the ruins of the Crusaders' castle at Athlit stood out against the narrow strip of grey, blue, or silver that was all we could see of the Mediterranean. Right across the plain the fellahin tilled their small plots of ruddy, fertile soil, leaning their thighs against the shank of the plough to turn the share while the oxen plodded softly to and fro. Each day from our terrace we could not fail to watch the sun rising in morning coolness behind the mountain, climbing to the high tyranny of noonday and dropping behind the sea; as these sun-measured days accumulated into seasons we saw the seasonal colour advance across the outstretched plain.

Early every morning a line of graceful, gaily dressed girls and a few fine, muscular young men set out from the neighbouring village to come to work for us. The girls in their tight-waisted, full-skirted dresses and long baggy trousers, their lunch-bundles poised on their heads, picked a way deftly across the rocks; the men strode along with more bravado, asserting their careless independence of the earth they trod. Soon a narrow path was worn between the village and the cave.

That morning procession of Arabs was impelled, and that path worn, by ideas grown in the inquisitive minds of Europe and America. These minds, belonging to individual men and women, were so caught up in the tide of curiosity about the physical universe that they pursued answers like a pack of hounds. They had run everything from microbes to the Milky Way, and now were in full cry after the answer to the question about themselves: what was the history of their own self-consciousness, how did these terrible and wonderful organs of thought, feeling, and imagination come to be on earth? How on earth?

The irresistible force of this curiosity had caught up every one of us in that party of explorers, driving us across land and sea to Palestine. Now we in turn moved others—others who knew not what they did. Tall intelligent Yusera, shrill Rashidi, the gazelle-eyed, poetic child Fatima and all the other girls were brought to the cave by the same compulsion of the mind that had once made old Francis Bacon climb down from his coach and provoke his death by stuffing a run-over chicken with snow. This impulse it was that made them sit in rings, the blues, pinks, and greens of their cotton dresses and trousers giving each circle of girls the appearance of a flower, employing their deft brown fingers to pick out the bones of gazelles, antelope, hippopotamus, and other beasts on which the ancient hunters had lived, and the flint implements their hands had shaped. This that made each girl in turn rise from her circle, balance a basket of discarded cave earth on her head and run with a sinuous grace along the terrace to tip these scourings of a remote past, briefly remembered, into the final oblivion of our spoil-heap. It brought the village headman, the devout Mahmoud who every evening spread his rug among the rocks and thorns and prayed eastward to Allah; it brought daredevil Akmet in his embroidered cap, forcing him to swing his pick till it sparked on the fallen boulders.

All of us working there on Carmel were the agents of this universal curiosity—its willing but helpless agents.

Down and down we went through the off-scourings of time, in a few weeks stripping off the silted layers which had taken tens of thousands of years to accumulate. They had fallen unnoticed, long before history, long even before words had begun to clarify the thoughts of man; now in turning them back we recorded all we could detect of the forgotten events of time past. In an attempt finally to pin them down, to rescue them once and for all from forgetfulness, we used the sound symbols, the letters of the alphabet, which had first been devised not so very far from this place many millennia after the cave had filled up and been deserted. So when steel picks and the lean, deft hands of the Arab girls had disengaged them, we took the flints which hunters had shaped to kill and cut up the warm bodies of antelope, wild horse, and hippopotamus and with a mapping pen marked them with letters in Indian ink, preparing them to be tabulated, interpreted, and fed into the maw of our curiosity. As we went down layer by layer the form of these tools changed, and so too did the species of the game animals, for all belonged to the flow of process where nothing can be constant.

At last, towards midwinter, we came upon the skeleton. It lay crouched on its side, the skeleton of a woman with low vaulted skull recalling the simian stock from which this race was lifting itself. Human consciousness had not been highly tempered when it was housed in that poor cranium, but now in us it was returning to discover, study, and reflect upon its ancient haunts. Flesh-covered hands used scalpel and brush to clean the delicate metacarpal fan of the bone hand; eyes charged with centuries of curiosity looked into the sockets of the skull.

I was conscious of this vanished woman and myself as part of an unbroken stream of consciousness, as two atoms in the inexorable process to which we belonged. I saw us as two atoms, but also, a little sickeningly, as two individuals; myself, the inheritor of a consciousness that seemed so profoundly and subtly personal, and this one-time mother of the tribe who must have lived and died hardly aware of past or future, yet who would surely have known fear, and even sadness, when at last her shambling body weakened and she had to lay it down. With her mind a wordless hollow swarming with impressions and emotions, she would not, like myself, have been condemned to live with the certainty of her death, but she would have felt some vague regret that she could no longer enjoy men or children or the saliva rising at the smell of venison. Perhaps even in her dim, unconcentrated mind she regretted spring and the beauty of the world.

With an imaginative effort it is possible to see the eternal present in which all days, all the seasons of the plain stand in an enduring unity. I hope in this book to show the whole of human becoming and being like a plant standing in eternity. But there is also a terrible reality in that opposing vision of the linear passage of time, of the continuous leaving behind which fills us with a cruel awareness of the wastage of our brief lives. Perhaps of all men the archaeologist must be most aware of time passing. He knows it so well because he has seen with his actual eyes and felt with his hands how the more recent tool will always lie above the older one; the bones of the grandchild above those of the grandparent. So, while we uncovered the skeleton detail by detail and then shrouded it in plaster of Paris, I often looked at it with sorrow.

The winter rains were unusually heavy that year; the dry wadi below the cave filled with a tearing stream and the soft soil of our dump (that which once had formed the layers of time) was soon fluted with miniature watercourses. Then, when the sun returned, all over the limestone slopes and the untilled verges of the plain, anemones pushed their crimson corollas through the grit. Never, until much later when I was to see the scarlet plumage of the cardinal birds that display themselves among the thorns and cactuses of Arizona, was I to experience anything comparable to the wonder I felt that life could draw such intensity, such richness and beauty from among the stones. Just as consciousness has intensified within the human skull, so has this marvellous redness, sucked incomprehensibly from the harshest desert, intensified in feather and petal.

Meanwhile the Carmel tortoises provided the necessary comic aspect of the eros which lies behind this intensification of mind and colour and all the other high creations of life on earth. The rain had roused the anemones, and it seemed also to stir the erotic impulse of these reptiles, setting them to make love in the prickly tunnels below the camel thorn. One could hear the rattling of horny shells as the males mounted the females, and anyone inquisitive enough to peer through the thorns could laugh at the ridiculous antics of a species for which nature has provided such ample security that creation is all but prohibited. Flat base of the carapace rattled and slid upon curved roof while the symbol of life darted vainly. However, at last all was accomplished and it was assured that little tortoises would presently break out from leathery eggs in total ignorance of the problem before them.

One night when the land was still fresh from the rain, I was wandering near our camp enjoying the moonlight when an intense exaltation took possession of me. It was as though the White Goddess of the moon had thrown some bewitching power into her rays. It seemed to me that our arid satellite was itself a living presence bounding in the sky—I do not myself understand this use of the word 'bounding', but it comes insistently, and I cannot but use it to express some deeply felt vitality. Indeed, the whole night was dancing about me.

It appeared that the moonlight had ceased to be a physical thing and now represented a state of illumination in my own mind. As here in the night landscape the steady white light threw every olive leaf and pebble into sharp relief, so it seemed that my thoughts and feelings had been given an extraordinary clarity and truth.

So powerfully was I moved by this sense of possession that I climbed up on to a high outcrop of rock against the mouth of the wadi and knelt down there. The moonlight swam round, and in, my head as I knelt looking across the plain to the shining silver bar of the Mediterranean.

From far behind me, still muffled in the folds of the mountain, I heard the bronze sound of camel-bells. To my sharpened but converging senses they seemed like a row of brown flowers blooming in the moonlight. In truth the sound of bells came from nothing more remarkable than a caravan, perhaps twenty camels with packs and riders, coming down the wadi on its way northward to Haifa. But even now I cannot recognize that caravan in such everyday terms; my memory of it is dreamlike, yet embodies one of the most intense sensuous and emotional experiences of my life. For those minutes, and I have no notion how many they were, I had the heightened sensibility of one passionately in love and with it the power to transmute all that the senses perceived into symbols of burning significance. This surely is one of the best rewards of humanity. To be filled with comprehension of the beauty and marvellous complexity of the physical world, and for this happy excitement of the senses to lead directly into an awareness of spiritual significance. The fact that such experience comes most surely with love, with possession by the creative eros, suggests that it belongs near the root of our mystery. Certainly it grants man a state of mind in which I believe he must come more and more to live: a mood of intensely conscious individuality which serves only to strengthen an intense consciousness of unity with all being. His mind is one infinitesimal node in the mind present throughout all being, just as his body shares in the unity of matter.

The bells came nearer and another sound mingled with theirs; a low, monotonous chanting. I looked behind me for a moment and saw the dark procession swaying out from behind the last bend in the wadi. Then I turned back so that the column should pass me and enter my world of vision from behind. I found myself comprehending every physical fact of their passage as though it were a part of my own existence.

I knew how the big soft feet of the camels pressed down upon and embraced the rough stones of the path; I knew the warm depth of their fur and the friction upon it of leather harness and the legs of the riders; I knew the blood flowing through the bodies of men and beasts and thought of it as echoing the life of the anemones which now showed black among the rocks around me. The sound of bells and the chanting seemed rich and glowing as the stuff of the caravan itself.

So the swaying line came from behind, went past, and moved away across the plain. It was a procession of life moving through the icy moonlight. It was coming from the mountain and going towards the sea. That was all I knew, but as the moon leapt and bounded in the sky I took full possession of a love and confidence that have not yet forsaken me.

Before very many years I was myself more directly caught up in the workings of process. I do not think that any male can ever know and accept this participation with the poignancy that a pregnant woman is forced to know and accept it. No wonder that in all societies, from the most primitive to the most finely civilized, woman is recognized as representing the earth and its darkness; she belongs to this planet from which in fact we have all grown, while man feels himself something of a stranger, looking for a source of his spirit in some other realm. No matter if she wears ruffles, or swans in her hair, inwardly woman understands her earthiness.

The male knows he must grow old and die, but this knowledge can never command the immediate submission to process that is a necessary part of childbearing. Once the sperm (a most primitive form of life) has swum to its goal, a female knows that relentlessly, inside a body which hitherto she has regarded as being in a sense herself, cells are going to divide, proliferate, and specialize to a pattern determined half a million years ago. She knows this will happen quite apart from her wishes: whether she delights in it or resists it. She may busy herself knitting woolly bootees or hemming nappies, she may go to the most aggressively ordinary department store for her expanding maternity gowns, but still she is aware that this is no tame domestic affair which has caught her by the hair. She is forced to see that this body which has gone about the world with her name attached to it, this body with whose idiosyncracies of form and colour she is so familiar from her looking glass, this physical self, is now the slave of some great and marvellous and absolutely tyrannical purpose of which neither she nor he who launched the sperm has been vouchsafed any understanding.

Month after month when she looks down along her body in bed or bath she must watch what was once *her* belly swell as inexorably as a melon in the sun. Then muscles which she had supposed were in her control begin to play the devil and she must throw out a new unit of life in the blood and tears and sweat which men like Winston Churchill can afford to associate with an act of volition.

What can force home even more powerfully an acceptance of the truth that she is participating in some vast and impersonal process is the historical element in pregnancy. All the stages through which the foetus within her must grow link it, and therefore her own being, with far simpler and more primitive forms of life. They appear there in her womb as a legacy from the remote past; but related forms exist still in rivers and jungles and other places with which she would not normally identify herself.

For the first few weeks the tiny creature embedded so securely in the uterus can be linked with the historical beginnings of life when the sun first generated it in sea or mud, or with some of the simpler creatures of modern ponds and ditches. Then, as is well known, the foetus develops the gill pouches of our fishy ancestors of three hundred million years ago; at about the third month it has a tail, a fitting inheritance from the days when common ancestors of ours and the apes and monkeys swung blithely in trees; until only a few weeks before its mother projects it into a world of cotton-wool and Dettol the little beast has head hair extending lovably but inhumanly down on to its face.

So, it may happen that a girl too dull to grasp 1066 comes to enact within her body, on the stage supported by her bony skeleton, events recalling this colossal procession of history, this biological pageant of five hundred million years.

How fascinating to contemplate, then, is the act which initiates this drama, and how close it evidently lies to the heart of the human predicament. Two lovers are attracted to one another, it may be at first by the shared pursuit of poetry or music (or even, heaven help them, by crystallography and mathematics) or by some other of the highest achievements of the human consciousness of the last thousand years. Then perhaps this man and woman find grown within them a tremendous love and understanding for the essential John and the essential Sophia, two individuals unique in history and most exquisitely and particularly themselves. But soon the imperious and impersonal eros, which all along has been lurking somewhere below the surface like an ant-lion in the sand, proclaims itself and taking hold of the two who have come together through poetry and individuality throws them on to bed or floor. As their passion proceeds John and Sophia are all but evicted from their bodies; the ant-lion sees to that, for he needs those bodies as the blind and helpless minions of his power. It is only when the sperm have swum off on the mission which may begin the rehearsal of life on earth that John and Sophia are allowed to return to their bodies, taking possession of them again in a bewildered haze of tenderness. It is an ironical aside on this business that the younger the lovers are, the more idealistic, the more completely are they lost. Their elders with a longer experience of individuality have a firmer anchorage in it, and even while their bodies are swirled through the timeless caverns of passion may dimly apprehend their own particularity.

After the fruitful act of passion comes the sexual parting of the ways; the woman must go to accept her unity with earth and play her part in process, while man hurries off shaking earth from his feet—a creature apart.

So in love, the relationship and the passion, human beings must experience the strange encounter between the individual and the unit of process, and experience it in a drama where its force is infinitely magnified by intensity of feeling. They must allow the ancient flood of their unconscious being to well up and submerge all the possession of mind and spirit that has been most strenuously worked for and most cherished. It is true that mind and spirit are refreshed by the inundation and tend to wither or grow stunted without it; it is true, too, that their existence makes human love perhaps the best achievement of the earth. Yet the experience of the inundation is a shock to individuality and its exclusive pride. No wonder that our species is fearful of physical love, goes to it as secretly as birds to death in the roots of a hedge. Here we must meet our past, leave the familiar little room with our name on the door and plunge back into the undifferentiated. No wonder that John and Sophia are bewildered, for they know they are born mortal and are unwilling (it is to their credit it should be so) to have this form of immortality thrust upon them by the ant-lion.

It is no wonder that we are fearful of love and yet know it for our greatest solace. Eros must come together with Psyche; we must return to the past in order to make the future—and while we are engaged in it how appropriate that time should be defeated. Love can make John and Sophia recognize their kinship with ape, fish, and rock—and for that matter with the comic tortoise of life. It is good to make some excursion from the room with the name on the door before one has to leave it in a coffin with a name now vainly inscribed upon the lid.

backbone 2

The body is roughed-out

Is it possible today for any unprejudiced and intelligent person to believe in the orthodox view of the workings of evolution? Can such a person believe that we and all our fellow travellers in life from apes to algae have been shaped and coloured and endowed with our highly distinctive habits by natural selection alone? For my part I am convinced that although the development of life and its species has taken place exactly as the geologists and biologists have discovered since the evolutionary process brought these scientists into being, they are utterly mistaken in their explanation of how it took place. When devising their doctrine of the evolution of species by natural selection, they were guilty, so I believe, of focusing their whole attention on the fringes of a movement so vast that they entirely overlooked it.

If such people were observing the growth of an acorn newly seeded in a wood and saw how the tree grew a little lop-sided because of the infringement of a neighbour, turned yellow on the south side because of the sun and lost a branch on the north because of damp and fungus, then, so it seems to me, they would claim that the neighbouring tree, the sun, and the damp had determined the growth of the acorn into the oak.

Surely instead we must believe that life on this planet, and doubtless elsewhere too, is led along its evolutionary way by some force of design comparable to that which determines that the simple little oval nut so snug in its cup shall, if given opportunity, grow into a forest tree. Natural selection has done no more than modify the trivialities of the process. I believe there to be some such shaping force at work behind what is happening on this planet, but I certainly do not believe it to be as precisely predetermined as the oak tree within the germ of the acorn. It seems clear to me (perhaps because I cannot help possessing the simple kind of female optimism) that each species has the freedom to create its own highest potentiality or to fail to achieve it. The instrument is a persistent eros in which the polarity of sex plays a great and noble part, but which also has many other forms. Not only do males and females drive one another to lovelier colours, finer songs, higher imagination, but insects provoke flowers to brighter, more alluring endeavour, animals of prey are provoked by the skill and perfection of the pursued; the nightingale, I dare say, is egged on by the moon, and man by the whole universe as he discovers it. And in the working of this eros, this tissue of urges passing to and fro through all being, each living kind has its own duty. The duty of man, the hero of this book, is the heightening of consciousness. That is plain enough.

I had long hesitated over my refusal to credit the orthodoxy of evolution, when one day a visit to South Kensington settled the matter for me. As I am one of the most visually minded of human beings, it was the sense of sight which finally convinced a wavering intelligence. I was walking towards the new Bird Hall when I found myself before a much older exhibit of the Natural History Museum, but one which I saw suddenly with fresh eyes. It was a case containing an Argus pheasant in full courtship display. Here was grotesque fancy, magnificence, and superb ingenuity. The fanned and whorled wings and tail, the curiously writhen stance of the bird produced a fine and energetic baroque. It was a tempest of feathers, a riot of plumage, and within it all the poor little cock bird who would look just as we know he would look if plucked, roasted, and set on toast.

Looking more closely I examined each participating feather. What perfection of detail! Set along the dove-coloured silk of the plume were the Argus eyes, ruddy and shaded to give an effect of false relief so that every eye stood out like a gem *en cabochon*.

Then, round legs and tail, peeping out from below the more dashing plumage, an absurd flurry of white underfeathers, for all the world like the frothy underwear of a gay Edwardian.

Standing in front of this prodigious fantasy of nature I found certainty had taken possession of me: the sexual selection of the hen standing primly near her mate could never even in millions of years have conjured up so wonderful a creation. Dear, demure hen pheasant, how could your natural preference for some dash and pretence in your mate produce this creation which would put Le Roi Soleil quite in the shade?

As a clinching argument, had one been necessary, in the neighbouring case I saw a brilliant crimson bird from whose rear there soared and then drooped in graceful parabola a pair of fantastically elongated feather shafts tipped with a tiny pennon of plume. Could female selective susceptibility draw out these fluttering streamers? Surely not, and certainly such fripperies would be a handicap in the struggle for existence.

From that moment in the Natural History Museum I was not only intellectually but also intuitively and emotionally convinced that the accepted doctrine of evolution misses the main power behind it. This power is so huge and so obvious that it cannot be discovered by the little knives of analysis and for this reason the scientists fail to recognize it. One cannot see landscape through a microscope.

If we approach the process from the other end, assuming a godlike power to accelerate the passage of time, until a thousand ages in our sight endures less than a minute, creation by natural selection still fails, so far as I am concerned, to appear any more convincing. As I make the effort to see thousands of generations following one another, and the best fitted, selected by differential death and breeding for survival, giving rise at last to the multifarious world we know, I find a score of problems barring the way to acceptance.

First of all, one form of selection would so often seem to oppose another: sexual selection, say, working against protection from enemies. It is easy, for instance, to picture a million generations of lizards with snakes and other enemies always inclined to spare the individuals which had a larger horny carapace, and so gradually giving rise to the closed shop of the fully evolved tortoise. On the other hand would not the survival value of the shell be more than offset by the difficult and dangerous mating habits which it made inevitable? Then there is the question of how characters were evolved which were entirely useless until their evolution was complete. The woodpecker's stout bill and neck enable it to nest in comparative safety in the chamber it can carve in a branch, but what happened when the hammer head was only stout enough to begin a small and quite unpractical boring? There is the recognized problem of evolutionary trends once started going too far and leading headlong to extinction, as with the dinosaurs and ammonites; there is the perfectionism, the attention to detail far in excess of what could be biologically effective—can the mark simulating a hole eaten by a grub on the wings of leaf-butterflies conceivably have been valuable enough as a protection to get itself established? Surely the perfect imitation of

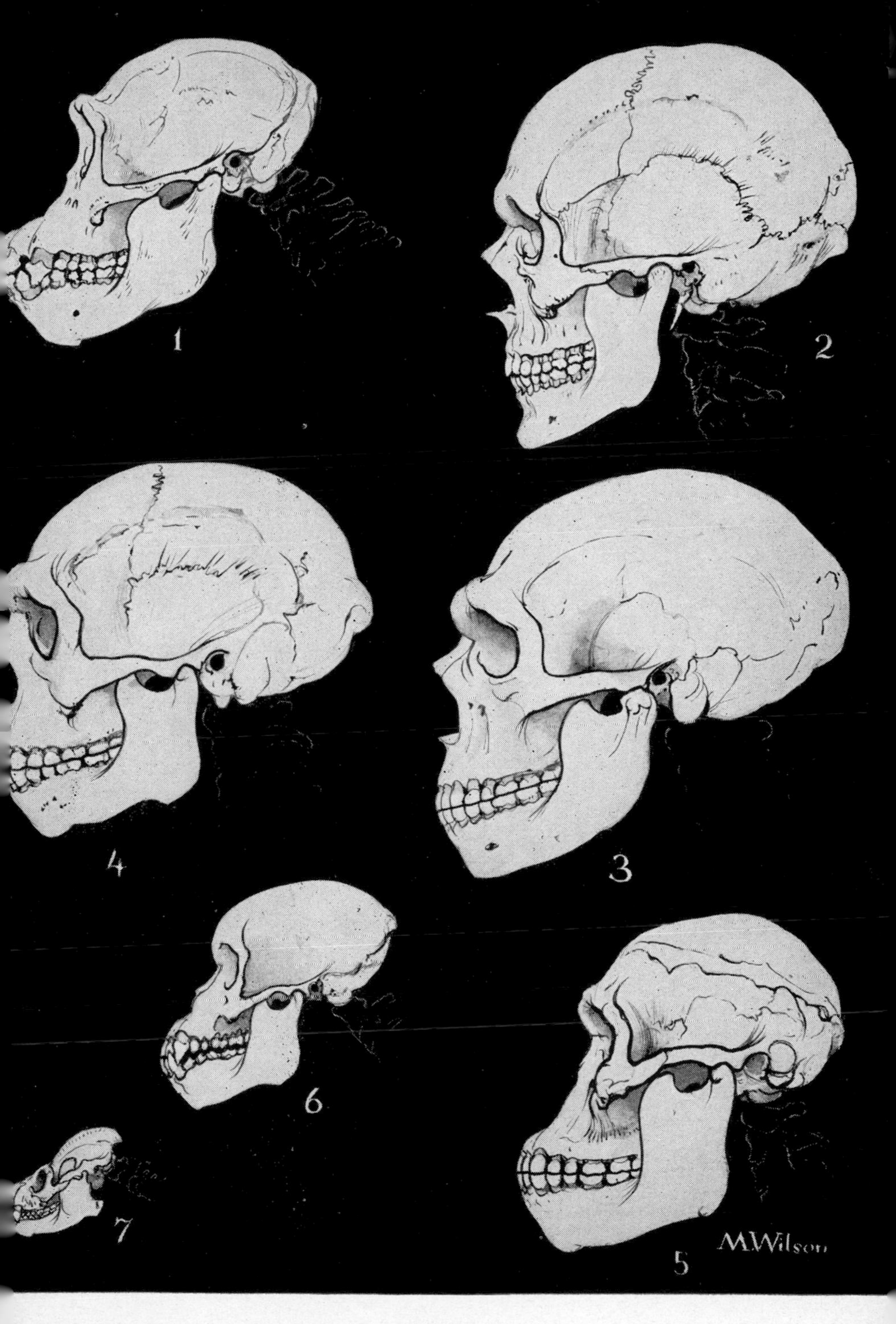

THE EVOLUTION OF MAN'S SKULL

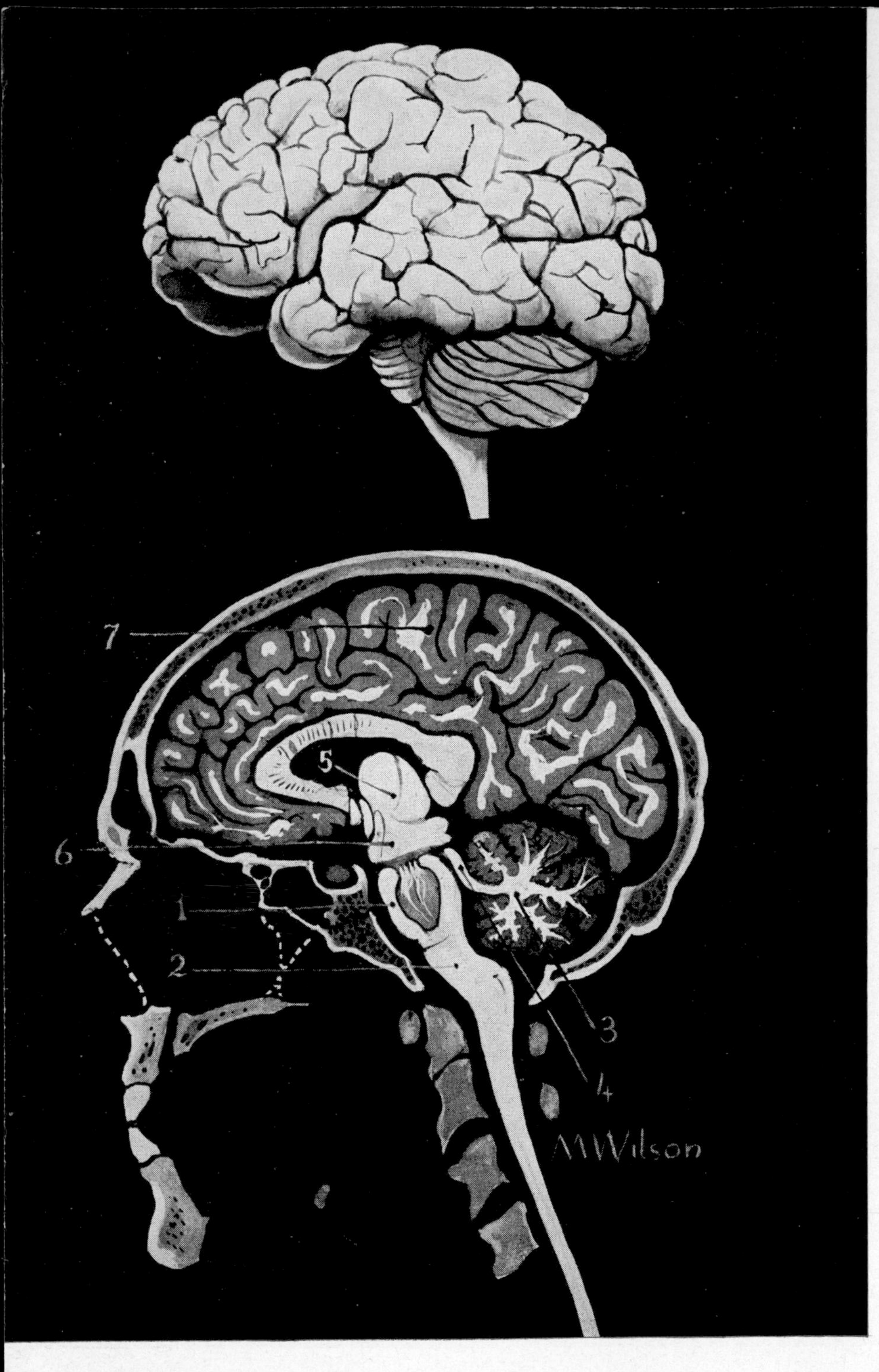

MAN'S BRAIN, SIDE VIEW AND SECTION

shape, stem, veins and colouring were already disguise enough?

Then again there is the problem of the extraordinarily various results of similar conditions of selection. Once in a Mexican forest I stepped out from deep shadow into a clearing large enough to allow a few sunbeams to penetrate. Encouraged by the light, a slender tree had put out a spray of purple trumpet-shaped flowers which were hanging half shaded, half in the sun. To my delight, there, poised before the spray, was a humming-bird; I could hear the tiny murmur of its invisible wings, and the plumage seemed to throw off sparks of emerald and gold. At my approach it darted off like a dragonfly and was quenched by the shadows. Now other species of humming-bird living there or in similar conditions might be crimson and blue or one blazing atom of purple instead of this emerald and gold, might possess crests, wing and tail pennons and all manner of exquisite but differing embellishments. How do these differences arise, and why in this particular group of birds is sexual selection able to conjure up results so incomparably brilliant? This leads back once more to the argument of the fantastic, wanton, unnecessary extravagance of nature as represented in the Argus pheasant.

But surely the strongest of all arguments is offered by the species which is the subject of this book. By what extraordinary series of chances has natural selection produced Shakespeare's poetry, Rembrandt's portraits, the music of Mozart, Einstein's powers of thought—or even the atom-splitters? If natural laws cease to apply when they have led to the creation of human culture, then this appears to me to be a highly unscientific conclusion, for why in a purely natural and chance process should there come this revolution in values? Yet everyone knows how often the highest, most glorious human faculties count against the survival and propagation of the genius possessing them, and to some extent this is true of whole peoples. Besides, the most improbable chances supposedly involved in shaping our ends are obvious again and again long before the growth of culture. For instance, life in the trees and a dainty vegetable diet are said to have been necessary for the evolution of our deft fingers and our keen, stereoscopic vision; yet it was also necessary for us to descend to the ground again and adopt a meat-eating habit in order for our deficiencies in tooth and claw to goad us into tool-making. How fortunate that the brain happened by this time to be ready to meet the challenge—and yet how extraordinary that the structure of the brain evolved by natural selection solely to enable an animal species to survive in the wilds of a mindless earth, should, in a few thousand years and without further structural change, prove both able and inclined to the practice of painting, poetry, music and pyramid-building.

I am well aware that biologists have replies of a kind to most of these arguments, but for me they are refuted when I look at humming-birds and Argus pheasants, at the whole fabulous extravagance of life in the air, on land, and under the water; most decisively of all when I think of the number of most peculiar chances intervening between the ancestral tree-shrew and William Shakespeare. I simply cannot explain our beautiful, surpassingly various and supremely imaginative world by the orthodox tenets of evolution. And when I examine those tenets themselves with all the care and objective reason I can command, I find them full of obscurities, evasions, and having things several ways at once. However, it is not at all my purpose to make my heterodoxy an important issue in this book. My purpose is to attempt to give an impression of what in fact has happened to our kind on earth, and here I am not in any way in disagreement with the findings of science and history. When the story lies exposed, it is for every reader to judge for himself what forces lie behind the narrative.

To this narrative I must now return, my immediate concern being to follow the emergence of our species through the hundred million or so years that are, very approximately, rehearsed during the nine prenatal months and the first fifteen years of post-natal life of the individual man. I choose the age of fifteen because I intend in the next three chapters to bring our history down to the last phase of the Old Stone Age, and I consider that a boy of fourteen roughly corresponds to that phase of talented and ingenious hunting life. After that, like Man, he begins to be civilized.

In attempting to describe this emergence I shall accept, as the human historian must, the inexorable laws of linear time, the irreversible succession of layer fallen upon layer that we found on Mount Carmel. But with this I shall hope to make it possible to look down through the dimension of time to see the whole of our existence from the beginning of earthly life standing in an undivided present. Often when thinking of the life of a human being, particularly of a great one of high achievement, we succeed in imagining it as a whole, seeing for example the child Mozart playing one of his precocious compositions and then frisking round the room on a hobby-horse as existing in one piece with the mature genius of Salzburg. With greater imaginative effort we can achieve the same unity for the life of Man.

While we can watch our species taking shape in time, rather as we look down upon a tree growing in a hollow below us, we must never allow ourselves to forget that it has not in fact grown up in isolation but always in intimate relationship with innumerable other forms. Springing from a common source, men and all the abounding life on this planet have grown up together, and if now we are set apart by our self-consciousness we can still recognize a lasting kinship with all our companions. Once we had close kin in little squirming shapeless creatures in the slime, then with fishes, with amphibians, reptiles, tree-shrews and primitive apes, and all these whilom near relations have their conservative descendants whom we can go out to meet and salute in ponds, sea-pools, deserts, and jungles. To pursue the human line of growth among all these others is comparable to pursuing that of a single family within a nation.

Our descent from a species resembling a tree-shrew has the same degree of continuity as the descent of Elizabeth II from King Egbert, but while in the royal lineage it is usually possible to trace it generation after generation through known individuals, in the lineage of man the direct ancestral species is often unknown. Again and again we know of an animal which we can say must have come from a common ancestor on the direct human line, but we do not know the ancestral form itself. It is as though Queen Elizabeth wished to collect a portrait gallery of her ancestors, but found that the pictures of father, grandfathers, great-grandfathers were all missing, obliging her to fill the gallery with cousins and collateral lines.

There is nothing mysterious about this; our ancestral species are often missing because no fossil has been found. The privilege of fossilization is rare for all creatures, depending as it does on a corpse falling into calm, quickly silting mud or any of the other far from common conditions that allow its preservation. Then, should it secure this form of immortality, the eruption of volcanoes, the titanic pressures of mountain-building, and the constant wear of water and wind may destroy it during the huge spans of later geological time. Then, too, we have not long been looking for such fossil portraits as do survive. Ever since men became self-conscious enough to feel troubled and wish to explain their presence in the world, different groups of them had answered the question by devising dramatic and beautiful or barbarous stories of an immediate divine creation. These myths prevailed for thousands of years; the new curiosity that looks for ancestral memories in the rocks has been at work for barely a century. The chances against our finding, in so short a time, the remains of many species that are our direct forebears are overwhelming. It is astonishing that our curiosity has already discovered as much as it has.

As for the history of all earthly life, in looking for our own beginnings we have to go back some thousand million years to the time when empty oceans washed upon bare rocky continents and there was nowhere a trace of life, no hint of how from this desolate landscape there would come Argus pheasant, love or lyric, hate or bomb. Our planet swung round the sun on its graceful orbit as it had done since its gases condensed to a molten mass, a crust formed upon it, and oceans formed upon the crust. It was not only void of active consciousness but of that capacity for organized growth and self-propagation that we now accept as the mark of life.

Although life and inorganic existence appear to be so sharply distinct, we have discovered them to run into one another almost without a break. In the line from rock to moving, sentient life there is no point where we can lay a finger and say on this side is life and on that no life. One of the forms making the transition from one to the other is the virus. It assumes the form of perfect crystals, seemingly as inorganic as any other crystalline structure, yet remains able to revert to a condition in which it can divide and multiply and so qualify, to the satisfaction of the most anxious analytical mind, as a living thing.

These viruses, when active, cannot be seen through a microscope or caught by filters, yet are powerful enough to cause some of the most cruel of human diseases. So it may be that the earliest forms of living matter generated by the sun on slime or sea-water resemble those which now choose a habitat in the human body, devastating whole nations with influenza, breaking hearts by the tragic devastation of paralysis.

At that time of the begetting of life by the sun out of the earth (how near some of the primitive human myths come to the 'scientific fact') not only was the possibility of tragedy remote by a thousand million years, but even the material forms life was to assume were so frail and formless as to leave few marks of their existence. We can picture the living world of the pre-Cambrian seas of over five hundred million years ago as hazy and dreamlike; little specks of protoplasm or larger masses, single-celled creatures and more complex ones drifted or swam in the waters, lay or wriggled in the mud—all of them intent only to get nourishment from sun, water, and one another. They had not developed the firm outline always so necessary if one is to make an impression in the world. Even the tenderest mud could not preserve forms so vague and intangible. Graphite represents elementary life in these oceans; there are faint imprints of worms and algae, and of a jelly-fish from rocks exposed deep in that astounding cut in the earth's crust—the Grand Canyon of Arizona. It is pleasing to reflect how this creature which, with its pale translucent parachute and trailing tentacles, swam through the pre-Cambrian seas until its faint glimmer of life left it and it sank into the mud, should have been exposed to human eyes by the great Colorado river after it had cut down through the mile-deep deposits of later ages. Below the tremendous walls of sandstones and limestones that glow like old bricks in the evening sun, the river has exposed harsh, dark rocks, the time-hardened remains of ancient mud, and there at the bottom of this section through the depths of time men return to find the imprint of a single jelly-fish.

We have been able to recall very little of the first ventures in bodily form, but two of the types of single-celled creatures that still swarm in the fresh waters of the entire world may be chosen as representing one of the important advances of these pioneers of life. The microscopic speck of protoplasm that is the amoeba is contained within a delicate membrane which has no fixed shape but allows the creature to creep about by protruding portions of its body as false limbs—as though a down pillow were galvanized to walk on its corners. Paramecium shows several advances on the humble amoeba, and these changes, though they may not be identical with those which took place in the early phases of life, certainly represent their general trend. The paramecium has achieved a firm, unalterable outline and one which differentiates between head and tail end; it also possesses a well-defined inlet for food and gullet. In this acquisition of shape, fore-and-aftness, and a mouth, the paramecium indicates some most necessary steps towards the evolution of ourselves.

Another most potent instrument of change has also already appeared in pre-Cambrian times. Such single-celled animals as the amoebae and paramecia would have propagated their kind by simple fission, but many more elaborate species had developed sexual reproduction. Some, indeed, retained the ability to produce offspring by budding from the parent body, even while they enjoyed a sex life—perhaps limited to certain seasons of the year; if this was so the sexual rhythm was the only response to the changing seasons on our bare, leafless earth. Many species, again, that knew sexual reproduction were hermaphrodite, and many had no sexual contact, the male spurting out sperm to reach the female egg by way of the water. But other forms, and among them probably very elementary ones such as our modern flat-worms, came face to face and secured fertilization by the intrusion of a male organ into a female tube. So here already in this dim and remote world was the dawn of that eros, that tension between male and female, which has been used by the force behind evolution, and which, as I believe, has given to all its possessors a degree of free action through creative effort. No wonder that a power and an activity already so far advanced five hundred million years ago should be able to overwhelm our Johns and Sophias and sweep them away into strange, impersonal realms.

Though the memories of it surviving in the rocks are so very few, living forms were growing more varied and individually more complex. This is proved by the relatively sudden appearance in rocks of the Cambrian age of a host of different creatures offering ancestral forms of all the main families of the invertebrates. When it is remembered that today when we are so conscious of our fellow vertebrates from frog to elephant and fish to giraffe, the spineless part of creation represents ninety-five out of every hundred of the species of the earth, it is obvious enough what decisive steps had already been taken before the Cambrian era. We begin suddenly to be able to recall these most ancient invertebrates because at about this time they began to secrete limy external skeletons or other kinds of well-drawn outline that have been more readily preserved for us in fossil form. Whether this firmer assertion of life was due to the absorption of more lime from the water and its inevitable deposition in shells and other coverings, or whether armour was put on then, as now, as a defence in endless fighting for survival, is not sure. What is sure is that it took place, so making it possible for us to read in the layers of the rock this record of our own beginnings.

The Cambrian oceans were widespread and in many regions shallow and warm, washing continents that were not only still empty of life but parched and desert. Many of the living forms that would be most conspicuous to any observer who could use one of those glass-bottom viewers to look not only through clear water but through time, would be of creatures anchored to the sea-bed, giving it the appearance of a submarine garden. Among these were the coralline sponges, now altogether extinct, great numbers of lamp shells, and early crinoids and cystids, animals related to sea-urchins but living on plant-like stems and looking like submarine tulips, open or in bud. The mobile creatures, the active inhabitants of these animal gardens and the sea around them, were already in rich variety; on the sea-floor crawled water-snails and gross sea-cucumbers—whose modern descendants provide *bêche-de-mer* for Chinese soups—trapping their prey in slimy mouths; starfish moved in stately fashion on innumerable hydraulic feet, medusas throbbed gracefully overhead, and above them, near the ocean surface, swam myriads of molluscs, like the existing sea-butterflies, with slender cornet-shaped shells. Most active and strongly drawn of them all, a thousand varieties of trilobites, ranging in size from mere specks to monsters of eighteen inches, swam among the gardens, scuttled on the floors, or burrowed in the mud. These trilobites were the most powerful and highly organized forms that life had as yet attained; in them already the central nervous system, the necessary mechanism for all heightening of consciousness, was subtle and complex; many species had well-fashioned eyes with a mosaic of tiny lenses.

Some of the soft-bodied creatures that have vanished from history probably had vision of a kind, but it seems probable that the trilobites were the first to be able to project within themselves a clear image of the world about them. For us in whom the sight of things is immediately linked with understanding, vision with cognition, it is difficult to imagine sight that affects action but has no faintest undertone of thought; difficult too, but most interesting, to try to compare this illumined instinctive existence with the similarly instinctive but dark, eyeless life of, say, a groping starfish.

Although in their day they were the lords of creation, the trilobites are remote from our human family line; rather they have kinship with such handsome but untalented crustaceans as the lobster and crab. It seems that the creatures of the Cambrian seas most nearly related to our line were the sea-cucumbers, the cystids, crinoids, and (known only a little later) the sea-urchins. It is not suggested that these echinoderms are among our direct forebears but that there was a common ancestor of theirs and ours in early Cambrian or even pre-Cambrian times. Perhaps when next any readers of mine come into contact with a sea-urchin when bathing, knowledge of this early kinship will help to allay their pain. The relationship is showed partly by an unmistakable family likeness between infant echinoderms and the young of some of the primitive chordates that are close to the vertebrate form, partly by a biochemical affinity. To contract their muscles, sea-urchins and starfish secrete creatine phosphates, as do all vertebrates, in contrast with the arginine employed by the invertebrates.

So it seems that the echinoderms help to unite the teeming kingdom of the invertebrates with the pre-eminent group of the chordates—comprising all the vertebrates from fish to man. For long, zoologists were unable to link the two, and this seeming barrier between them was even used as a proof of separate creations. We now know that the barrier was made only by our ignorance, our failure to recall this particular moment of history; the starfish, sea-cucumbers, their kin and their unknown ancestor have helped to link the spineless with the spined and so to confirm the continuity of all life.

In contemplating these remote antecedents of ours, it is strange to think that creatures very like them survive into our modern world—to be shattered by our depth-charges and atom bombs, to find lodging in our lost submarines. Most of the actual Cambrian species are extinct, but their descendants show startlingly little change; they have been reproducing themselves with the utmost conservatism while animals, birds, insects, and men have evolved their manifold marvels and beauties. Time for their kind and for the progressive species would seem to be altogether different in scale and meaning. If when walking along the shore one either sees a medusa in full panoply careening along through the water or, on the other hand (that is to say, the hand away from the sea), one notices the dirty brown jellies of their stranded bodies on the sand, then it is worth saluting the immense antiquity of this sort of creature, its astronomical seniority to ourselves. One might recall that fossil imprint on the dark rocks in the depths of the Grand Canyon. No archdeacon can ever hope to be so venerable as the jelly-fish.

Our aim now must be to follow the development of the backbone, the original growth of that vertebral column which has since become a favourite property of moral metaphor. This column, a chain of ingeniously jointed discs with bony arches above them, was to become the chief support of the bodies of fish, reptiles, birds, and mammals, but its most important function was to carry and protect the extended length of the central nerve which runs through the bony arches much as some great urban electricity main runs through its tunnel.

The perfection of the backbone and the nervous system centred on it is the dominant plot of our story for the hundred million or so years succeeding the Cambrian age. Between them they secured that an intricate system of nerves controlling the movements of the body and its perceptions of the outer world should be safely carried to their reception points in the brain, and that the brain's house, the head, could be balanced and pivoted upon the body. We shall see how this structure of discs and rings with its most precious freight was to support the ribs of fish and snake, allowing them to swim and wriggle, and to support not only the ribs but also the four limbs—legs, arms, and wings—of all the higher animals. Above all, as I have said, an ingenious peg and socket joint on the top vertebra of them all supported the head, the head which was gradually to become the centre of consciousness of the world.

Let anyone watching Queen Elizabeth of England as she bows to the crowds of her subjects, or a great conductor—Toscanini—turning his face subtly from instrument to instrument in a symphony orchestra, reflect that these graceful, controlled, and significant movements look back to the first amphibians that crawled from the water and had to hold up their heads in the lighter air.

More immediately this story is concerned with a little fish-like creature, called Jamoytius, whose remains, known from Silurian times, closely resemble the living and even more diminutive lancelets that abound in shallow sea all over the world and particularly off the China coasts, where they are netted like sprats for human consumption. Jamoytius belongs to the chordates, a phylum which includes all the vertebrates and also a few more primitive types such as Jamoytius itself. For this species had no true backbone but in its place a gelatinous rod enclosed in a tough sheaf with the main nerve running above it. This rod or notochord offered adequate support for the swimming muscles of a creature that possessed little else beyond an open mouth, well-developed blood and digestive system and an ability to bury itself in the sand when alarmed. Still there is no doubt that Jamoytius occupies a distinguished place in our history; there are, after all, many human beings alive today, both eminent and humble ones, whose approach to life is very similar. The distinction of Jamoytius and the modern lancelet is that they represent the primitive chordates from which the whole vertebrate line has sprung; all this line, including our own species, commemorates this descent by repeating the notochord form during an early phase of embryonic life.

Although the development of a fitting architecture for the central nervous system was the main theme of life at this time, for it was a most important step towards the self-consciousness of the world, the rest of existence did not stand still. In the seas of the Ordovician and Silurian Ages, disturbed from time to time by violent volcanic eruptions, the welling up of the molten rocks whose mighty power lies always in wait, marine life grew more abundant and varied. In particular the sea-gardens in the warm, clear, and shallow seas were enriched by the development of the corals. It taxes the imagination to appreciate fully these forms of life in which myriads of minute individual creatures together create a greater structure that seems to have its own individuality. This is true not only of the corals but also of all the sponges, the bryozoa, with their exquisite fans and other shapes, the graptolites now extinct but whose colonies then floated in great numbers on the surface of the sea. The coral polyps, so simple in structure that they are close to the most elementary forms of life, secrete round themselves a limy house, or external skeleton, and all the houses or skeletons build up upon one another in an exact architectural form, each species following its own design from delicate branching tracery to the solid domes of the brain corals. Each tiny creature, less than half an inch long, adds its form, like a single stone or brick in our human buildings, to a predetermined structure of infinite complexity and grace. One species could no more build itself into the architectural style of another than a Gothic mason could have built a Renaissance church.

The skeletal secretions of most corals are as white as our own bones, yet a coral reef can be brilliantly coloured. The colour is given by the polyps themselves, for their bodies are of many hues—soft pink or blue, yellow, green, or violet—and when they stretch out from their cells to feed it is as though a plant burst suddenly into bloom.

Meanwhile, though it was to be very long before they could rival the richness of these animal-gardens, true plant life was coming into its own. All through Cambrian times it had probably been limited to the sea, where, however, the red and green algae were already abundant and were probably manufacturing the oxygen necessary for any form of life on land. Our first recollection of land vegetation dates from the end of the Silurian Age, but already these fossils show plants well adapted to the revolutionary change from water to air. Some were smooth, and would have shown bright green as the sunlight showed through them, many were spiky like the species popular in the conservatories and parlour windows of fiercely defensive Victorian households, but by the end of Devonian times the fertile soils washed down from the new-formed mountains nourished a new and abundant vegetation. This already included the huge ferns, seed-ferns, and horsetails which were to make the undergrowth of the later Carboniferous forests. The horsetails, with their exquisitely jointed stems and whorls of leaves growing in lofty thickets, belonged to the family that still survives all over the world—though now in small and humble forms—spreading a primordial vegetation over railway cuttings, derelict factories, and bomb craters.

This then was the vegetable covering of the earth on to which, as we shall see, our ancestors first set fin. Already before the close of the Ordovician period there were near-fishes, strange creatures with big bony shields on their heads and upper bodies, jawless with mere slits for mouths. These plated freshwater ostracoderms were dominant during the Silurian Age, but their elaborate defensive armour, relatively as heavy and cumbersome as that of a fifteenth-century knight, proves that the evolving forms of life were already preying upon one another. Perhaps the chief terror of the Silurian sea- and river-beds was a gigantic relative of the lobster and the scorpion, a carnivore that might grow to nine feet in length and which paddled along its smoothly plated body with two cruel-looking claws extended in front of it, claws that could make a sudden thrust through a screen of waterweed and grip any unarmoured fish in their toothed pincers.

During the last four hundred million years there has never been a time when large numbers of the creatures of the earth, whether they are a few millimeters long or a hundred feet, have not been armed either for savage aggression or for defence. After this dragon of the invertebrates, there followed the huge armoured fish, and the flesh-eating reptiles, gigantic dinosaurs like Tyrannosaurus that represent the height of might and violence ever attained by thoughtless life. In their turn the early mammals developed fangs, tusks, and proliferating horns on a scale which almost approached the armature of the reptiles. Last in this series we must recognize ourselves. Ours is, I think, the only species that turns its weapons against itself, but in spite of this and in spite of the fact that we make our weapons instead of growing them, our participation in this general arming does seem to me to be another of the many common traits that link men with the universal trends of all life on earth. Our gladiators, knights, breast-plated guards, our thundering tanks, are not altogether unconnected with the ostracoderms who held their faint apprehensions of life below huge, bony helmets along the muddy river-beds of four hundred million years ago.

The backbone that has now been traced from an ancestor of the sea-cucumber through Jamoytius to the armoured near-fish made a tremendous advance during the succeeding Devonian Age. This was a period when the earth's crust, the basis of all life, was at its most unstable: rucking up into mountain ranges, and being split and holed by subterranean eruptions. Whether the rapid development of the vertebrates was stimulated by this disturbance of their surroundings—an early instance of challenge and response—who now shall say, but certainly it happened. There was an astonishing multiplication and development of fishes in the rivers and seas (now reduced in area by the lifting up of mountains); they were there in vast numbers and variety. The sudden and overwhelming ascendancy of the fishes in this age has been compared with that of the amphibians, the reptiles, the mammals, and of man in succeeding ones. The primitive jawless breeds were still abundant in fresh water, but many species of true fish had evolved by the middle of the Devonian age and some of them, including sharks, swam out to colonize the open seas. Some wore bony plates like their predecessors, but others were scaly; some had their all-important backbones made of cartilage, others of bone; there was an indescribable variety of the shapes of plates, scales, fins, spikes, barbels, of movement, expression, way of life. There was also an immense range in size, for preying upon the smaller sort were some terrible monsters with armour-plated heads and huge jaws equipped not with true teeth but with bony spikes that must have been sufficiently effective. One species, Dinichthys, grew to twenty feet in length, another, Titanichthys, outstripped it by another ten. Fossils of both these great fish of prey have been found below the foundations of the industrial city of Cleveland in Ohio; business men who had made their money there subscribed to have the fossils dug out, and the heavy bone jaws that had closed on so many fleeing victims of the Age of Fishes were brought to light and to the scrutiny of human curiosity by the steel jaws of mechanical excavators.

That in a relatively short time life should have assumed forms so huge as Dinichthys and Titanichthys is not so remarkable as it appears to us who are inclined to regard all other animals as having a fixed and significant size in relation to our own. Controlled as it is by glandular secretion, body size can vary more rapidly and with far less meaning than body form. There could easily be a race which from our height of six feet or so would be midgets, more diminutive than those whom our prejudice as to what is normal now drives towards the circus ring; a race whose houses were the size of dog-kennels but who surpassed us in intellect and feeling. Similarly some glandular change might shoot all mankind up to the height of circus giants and still have no effect upon our natures or capacities. We all know that cows and horses were the size of fox terriers only a few million years ago.

The great carnivorous fishes are significant for their place in the history of aggression, but they, like all their over-armed successors until our own day, did not survive very long. The future of the vertebrates never lay with them but with fishes that were smaller and more meek. Among these our ancestors were the Crossopterygii or fringed fishes, whose distant descendants have aroused so much excitement in the twentieth century. We were confident that all creatures of this kind had been extinct for seventy million years until the coelacanths were dragged up out of South African waters as though out of the depths of time. One had not long been on dry land, it will be remembered, before it was sharing a bedroom with a learned professor, a kinsman very many times removed. For the coelacanths with their fussy look, their excessive elaboration of fins and barbels, are in many ways very like the fringe-fin fish which may be said to have given rise to the whole population of land vertebrates from mice to men. They developed useful, bony teeth, and air sacs or lungs which could take over from the gills the crucial life-process of obtaining oxygen if the creature were stranded by retreating tides or prolonged drought. In addition, these gifted fish, who seem almost to have had an instinct for the shape of things to come, developed pairs of opposing fins both fore and aft which may first have been used for crawling on the sea-bed, but which in time enabled them to hobble through mud, and even to emerge boldly on dry land. These four fins, already visibly limb-like, lie behind our arms and legs—our skilful-tender arms, our strong-graceful legs. Let all craftsmen, athletes, ballet dancers, chorus girls, and lovers spare a thought for the Crossopterygii; they may all, and especially the lovers, find their provision of limbs inadequate to their imaginative ideals, but even so they, and indeed all of us, have reason to be appreciative of the founders of these useful and enjoyable members.

Indeed, it seems that the essential mechanism of fore and hind limbs more or less efficiently jointed to the backbone developed very fast. Already by the end of the Devonian there were true amphibians, and by the time the widespread, shallow, coralline seas of the earlier Carboniferous Age had given way to the swampy forest of the Coal Measures, life had produced creatures like clumsy salamanders and as much as ten feet long. A true amphibian is a beast which as an adult lives largely on land, perhaps gulping down its air supply, froglike, instead of breathing, but which enjoys an aquatic infancy, for the good reason that the female returns to the water to lay her eggs. Often, therefore, the infant amphibian is quite unlike the adult—a contrast well illustrated by the amphibians of today, all of them now small and humble creatures. I need hardly labour the difference between that jolly little wriggling gaper the tadpole, and the long-legged green bounder the frog. We have all observed it, and watched the transition with wonder and fascination, but perhaps have not thought of the historical aspect of the process—that the tadpole represents the ancestral habit. Our own species, as we have seen, has adopted a different timing, and one which allows human babies to be born already with a faint resemblance to men and women.

The young of Eryops and other amphibians that waddled and floundered through the mud, sandbanks, and decayed vegetable soil in the heavy, evergreen light below the coal forests, had gills, swimming fins, and fishy tails that made them differ from their parents almost as decidedly as tadpoles from frogs. When they suffered the metamorphosis from one stage to another, they not only lost gills and fins and grew effective ears in their heavy, bony, and still rather fish-like skulls, but also produced four limbs already astonishingly close to those of the mammals—including our own. That is to say each limb had a single stout upper bone articulating with the spine, and two much slighter lower bones articulating with the feet. Most remarkable of all, in many species these feet were provided with five toes, though there was a tendency, as there still is with mammals, for the front toes to be reduced to four.

I do not wish to grow wearisome by too persistent comparisons between ancestral forms and our own, but I must at this point beg some wonder—for the plain fact is wonderful indeed. The hand that holds pen, paint-brush, fiddle-bow, or scientific instrument is already most clearly recognizable in these feet that left their marks in the forest floors two hundred and fifty million years ago. Let anyone who wishes really to grasp and accept the continuity of life hold out his hand, look at it with unaccustomed eyes, feel its bones and nails, and see if, from somewhere at the base of memory, he cannot recover the feeling of the dark, warm mud squeezing between scaly claws.

Another particular bond between us is the Pineal Eye. Some of the amphibians had this third eye well developed, though already seemingly useless. We keep it still, a blind rudiment hidden in the darkness of the skull.

Now, in the time when the coal of our hearths, factories, and power-stations was accumulating layer by layer with the rotting of tree-ferns and scale trees, we have seen our forebears drag themselves up out of the water. With their action we abandoned submarine existence for ever, though we had by then imprisoned and have for ever kept the salt sea in our blood. We were never, like some other mammals, to return to the ocean as true members of its world; we waited until we had evolved ships, submarines, and diving suits and could visit it as alien explorers.

We had shuffled on fins, and now could waddle on legs a little less stumpy than a crocodile's—and on our five toes. Having thus got us safely on to dry land, I will uncurl my own five digits from the pen and end this chapter with the first two hundred and fifty million years of our life in time: the aqueous years.

blood 3

The body is warmed

With our ancestors on dry land and already in possession of the skeletal framework that still supports us, the main theme of this history moves up from the spinal column and its central nerve to the head it carries. With a central nervous system ready to serve it, the brain could now advance towards full consciousness. It became the depository of messages received from the organs of the five senses, the office from which inexorable directives were issued along the nerves. It formed for the body more and more of the innate habits of command and response we call instincts. Instinct represents memory grown automatic. It may be that already now the brain was beginning to store those other kinds of memory which concern experience unrelated to action, burying them deep where we, their inheritors, can sometimes draw upon them. What reptiles and shrews and apes saw and touched and heard may now find expression and recognition in the forms, colours, textures, and sounds of our most exalted arts.

Plainly air was a better element than water for the enlivenment of brain. Water must always, surely, be dimming, blurring: softening the impact of the outside world on the senses of its inhabitants, even while it dandles their bodies, making movement smooth and effortless. Anyone who has lain idly floating in a full bath and remained there while it empties, leaving the limbs heavy and unwilling to move, can understand the new bodily effort required of the amphibians when they left the embrace of the waters. Their response, the development of the skeleton with four legs to lift the body off the ground and ribs and breastbone to support the dead weight of the viscera, in time made possible a far greater variety of movement. From the subtle gliding of a snake to the bounding of a gazelle and bird flight, land and air made way for a rich variety of bodily exercise.

Everything on land would bring greater rewards and greater pain, for the reason that the senses were heightened and extended. So the smell of warm mud and vegetation, the sound of a passing dragonfly some day to be snapped and swallowed, the strike of hot sun on scales, the sensations of mating, are all more pleasurable than their submarine equivalents. Similarly to be gulped down by Titanichthys in the deep must have been far less painful than to be devoured by Tyrannosaurus in sun and air.

I do not hesitate to speak of the pleasurable and painful experiences of reptiles because I am convinced that in their direct emotional experience of living these precursors of ours, equally with our fellow animals today, have more in common with us than we care to admit. The development of our brains in the last million years by making us self-conscious and addicted to conceptual thought has made us forgetful of the common inheritance of feeling still naturally shared with the thoughtless animals that once we were. It is hard to cut away our habits of reflection and so recapture what we hold in common; lying in the sun I needs must think how it is hotter than it was yesterday, how it is good for me as a source of Vitamin C, how I wish it could always remain like this. But if basking in the sun makes me fall asleep there may, perhaps, be a drowsy moment between waking and sleeping when I can know the sensuous pleasure of a sentient body in the sunshine with direct emotion quite unencumbered by thought.

Thus while it can be idiotic to be sentimental about animals, for a series of feelings without conscious relationship or implication, without reference to past and future cannot produce anything comparable to full human sentiment, yet we should not feel quite cut off from them. Life is continuous from them to us; they form that part of our natural matrix fitting closest to our being; through them we can feel our unity with all that is. Our forerunners knew appetite, fear, pain, and a kind of vital well-being or exuberance, and so also do the creatures that have travelled through time with us. They cannot taste grief, despair, or joy, those are among the products of cerebral evolution, but they share in our more elementary emotions as surely as they share in our bodily inheritance of flesh, bones, and organs. We are not so lonely as we feel.

Orthodox evolutionists explain how existence on land, and presently in the trees, led to a sharpening of the senses, especially those of sight and touch, and how these active senses developed the brain; I should prefer to say that the vertebrates colonized the land in order that their senses might be refined and their brains develop. During the Permian and Triassic Ages our ancestral line passed from the amphibia to the reptiles and then to mammal-like reptiles. The neck lengthened, acquiring the seven vertebrae round which we still fasten our collars and hang our pearls. The structure of the ear was elaborated to allow more delicate sensitivity, while the growth of palatal bones dividing nose and throat must also have made the sense of smell more subtle. The reptilian eye was hard and keen.

Food for the senses was becoming always more abundant. Life was multiplying its sights, sounds, and smells even while it perfected the instruments for recording them. Where there was water, reptiles could look up at fringed tongues of the fern trees and dark tassels of the newly-appeared conifers moving against hot blue skies; they could see many kinds of fellow creatures living about them, perhaps representing food, perhaps death; they could even look into pools and have some inkling of their own image —a symbolic prelude to human self-consciousness. The reptilian eye must have sharpened itself most keenly on swift-moving insects. We know the terrible intensity with which a lizard will watch a fly; the snap of the jaws or dart of the tongue which follows seems like the release of an electric charge. One has a feeling of minute precision as much in the eye and nerves of the reptile as in the structure of the insects themselves.

Among the many varieties of insects then emerging came such familiar creatures as bugs, beetles, and cicadas; cockroaches were already in existence. Here are the insects that have since moved into our environment, whether we associate them with dirty beds and kitchens or with the lovely Mediterranean nights when the song of the cicadas under the moon seems to form a shimmering ocean of sound. They were there already in the Permian world with its deserts and mightily towering young mountains, its sudden glaciers and great dead seas where the water evaporated, fish became stunted and then extinct, until at last dried hollows filled with salt were left to harden beneath the sun.

As the Permian Age gave way to the Triassic, many of the ancient species died out, making way for successors with a vast and expansive future before them. It was already in the air, the hot Triassic air, that the reptiles were about to suffer an expansion, though no one viewing (no one did) the modest lizards and crocodile-like beasts of the time, seldom more than ten feet long and generally very much less, could have foretold the fantastic physical dominion that was opening before them.

Even more obscure because far longer delayed was the future of those reptiles, most of them of the smaller, humbler sort, now already evolving towards the mammalian idea. The mammal-like reptiles unhappily abandoned the conical reptilian teeth which replace themselves at need and developed that range of incisors, canines, and molars which in a few hundred million years were to provide material for a thriving race of dentists. More important still, some probably began to warm their blood streams and so acquired a greater independence of the outer world. We have seen how much of the success of all creation depends on firmness of outline. The Cambrian creatures acquired a firm outline which gave them strength not only in their own day but also to leave their fossil memories in the rocks. Then animal life came ashore where it exchanged the dreaminess and blur of submarine existence for the sharper definition of the air. Now the more progressive of the reptiles were to outgrow a dependence on the temperature of the air, which kept their bodies fluctuating with the dictates of sun and frost like any piece of rock. By an ingenious conservation of energy controlled by radiation through the skin they created inside the outline of the individual animal a fixed temperature, a private inner climate of its own, which it could carry through frost or fierce sunshine. This possession of a stable climate made possible the finer adjustment of many of the intricate mechanisms of living. Above all it was necessary for the exquisite adjustments for the working of the brain carried far by the mammals and ultimately to lead to the hegemony of man. Man himself has carried this isolation of the body much further. The modern American air-conditioned and thermostatically regulated house puts a second outline round man to enable his heat-controlled body to move in a heat-controlled envelope, completely cut off from the assaults of summer and winter.

But temples of gracious living, and indeed even the most uncomfortable human cave-dwellings, were still remote beyond understanding. The evolutionary process that must in any conditions have taken vast stretches of time to achieve humanity seems to have been delayed by another life drama which had first to hold the stage. Hitherto, although representatives of our ancestral line were normally to be found among the smaller and less specialized members of the dominant animal group of each age, they did belong to the dominant group. Not since the trilobites had formed the nobility of Cambrian life, while the forerunners of the vertebrates were of humble rank, had our ancestors occupied such a lowly position in the scale of life, far removed from the existing lords of creation. As sometimes the work of a great original artist or a new artistic trend must wait for its flowering until an earlier movement has exhausted itself, so now the mammals, already in being by the end of the Triassic Age, had to bide their time during the long, fantastic, and tyrannical ascendancy of the reptiles. Delayed with them is the main theme of this history, the development of brain as the dwelling-place of mind. For it was in their small, warm skulls, not in the massive, chilly caverns of the reptilian head, that the germ of future self-consciousness lay.

If, as is probable, the Triassic mammals emerged from the reptiles in South Africa, they must quickly have colonized most of the globe. By the Jurassic Age they were living in Europe and America. In Britain, for example, their fragile remains have been found in the Stonesfield limestone, later to be much sought after by their descendants for roofing tiles. Thus in the eighteenth century families must have lived below roofs in which these faint ancestral memories lay concealed—perhaps a single minute tooth, perhaps part of a tiny maxilla, once belonging to the little animals which prepared the way for man some one hundred and fifty million years before.

The early mammals were widespread but puny. As mice and rats occupy a house, establishing their own domain and habits, yet have to adapt them to the life pattern of the human occupants, so all through the long spans of Jurassic and Cretaceous Ages the primitive mammals had to fit in as best they could among the dinosaurs and other huge reptiles that were in possession of the earth. The analogy is closer than might at first appear, for these small self-effacing mammals were, many of them, very like rats and mice; particularly the tree-shrews that are on the direct ancestral line. So, if we like to play with time, the human householders who now dominate the lives of rats and mice were themselves in an earlier incarnation the rats and mice dominated by reptiles. As for the reptiles, they, on this same turn of the wheel, have fallen low, but, scorning to fit into the human pattern, they have sought deserts and swamps and have become, many of them, as hostile to all life as the serpent in Eden; cold-blooded poisoners. Life has its round dances as well as its advancing columns. It also has its lotus-eaters. Such (not of course speaking botano-zoologically) are the marsupials—primitive mammals which have survived to our day in Australia, South America, and other places where the competition has not been too fierce. How fortunate that there are such backwaters, because the modern world and its zoos and toyshops would seem a much poorer place, especially to children, without opossums, koalas, wallabies, and kangaroos.

While the mammals, little incubators of mind, waited meekly, feeding off nuts, fruits, shoots, insects, and other unwanted trifles, the reptiles advanced to achieve the greatest living might ever known on earth. Tremendous bodily size, tremendous bodily strength and ferocity, an astonishing variety of bodily forms from sea-lion sleek to spiked, horned, grotesquely armoured. In the oceans, then widespread and generally warm and clear, ichthyosaurs and mososaurs administered death with their long, tooth-lined snouts; in the air the pterodactyls might have been the models, recalled by man from the depths of memory, for his leathery-winged devils, the evil creatures whose profession it was to pitchfork sinners into the jaws of hell. Here is another seemingly fabulous piece of evolutionary history, that a creature should be able to thrust out its fingers, fingers starting very much like our own, until they were long enough to carry a ten-foot leathern wing.

As for the dinosaurs that had no rivals but one another for command of the land, surely their variety and elaboration, their reckless way of putting forth spikes, nobs, plates, and all manner of unnecessary exercises in ferocity of aspect, must repeat the evolutionary message of the Argus pheasant. But while the bird expresses the brilliance and decorativeness

MAN AS HUNTER

"The ornamentation of the person comes close to the bone of human nature."

"Man sees himself as he is, yet loves what he sees."

THE VILLAGE MAYOR: EGYPTIAN OLD KINGDOM

that is the prime goal of the avian eros, the dinosaurs had to express brute size and force. Some, like the colossal Diplodocus that could only support its thirty tons by living up to the neck in water, represented physical bulk alone, for they were as mild as lambs. Others, a Stegosaurus or Scolosaurus, were actors miming ferocity with appropriate properties in the form of spikes, nobs, plates, and claws, yet in fact were vegetarians, living harmlessly enough browsing on vegetation round the margin of warm lagoons.

If even the pacific dinosaurs had to express physical might in some form, the carnivorous species could represent mindless violence at its most cruel. Beyond the rest, it was incarnate in Tyrannosaurus. A man standing before this monster would hardly have reached to the knee of the taloned hind legs on which it strode; he would have had to look up some fifteen feet to the terrible head, its hellish jaws set with six-inch fangs, each one of them saw-edged to sear through flesh and bone. If the reptile stooped down, snatched up the man and held him in the clawed hands so evidently related to his own, it could bite through the thickest part of his body so easily that it would hardly notice the slight resistance to its fangs. Perhaps before they were fully grown, young Tyrannosaurs did not scorn to snap up any little mammals they might catch unawares, but the fully-grown brutes must have preyed on other dinosaurs, particularly the large plant-eating kinds. In fact, then as always the fiercest, most aggressive forms of life drew their force ultimately from the sun's energy where it lies entrapped through the chlorophyll of plants. If it is part of man's highest obligation to turn vegetable life into art, the business of

Tyrannosaurus was to turn it into pure ferocity.

It was almost the pure essence of ferocity. These monsters with an egg-sized brain lodged in the great cavernous skull received the messages from eyes, ears, and nose with as little thought as a cinema screen receives the images cast upon it. We are accustomed to the predatory mammals still inhabiting the earth with us, and incline to think of them as terrible but heroic; even noble. But with these reptiles there was no decision to follow a trail, no careful stalking or lying in wait, no calculated spring. Just the reception of stimuli and titanic, naked reaction.

During the ascendancy of the dinosaurs the conditions in many regions of the earth must have been, for a dinosaur, idyllic; the climate was mild or approaching tropical, there was abundant vegetation, there were lakes, lagoons, and swampy rivers. There were no violent upheavals of the earth's crust; while limestone and chalk accumulated with immeasurable slowness in clear, untroubled seas, the reptile shapes grew larger, fantasticated, fulfilled their mission of brutal force as though in a vast, quiet tank of time. Then suddenly, as suddenness is calculated in relation to the hundred million years of their heydays, they collapsed, were extinguished. The dinosaurs vanished from the earth until man recalled them, pulling out huge bones from the soft lias, from limestone, from chalk.

Having recalled them, one species after another since 1824 when Mary Anning found the first megalosaur in the cliffs at Lyme Regis, men have used their memory in one of two ways. Either they have said to themselves: 'We men are rash to boast of our supremacy in evolution when we have existed only for a million years, while the reptiles held sway more than a hundred times as long'; or they have said: 'The dinosaurs seemed invincible, but in fact they had taken a wrong turning; their mighty armature was useless; they were failures.' To me both morals seem equally at fault. If we can view our own species as existing plant-like in time, so, too, we can see the gigantic growth of the reptiles standing complete, perfected, in the clear air of the Jurassic and Cretaceous Ages. The sun shines upon it, there is a background of lagoons, coral atolls, lush and succulent foliage. The dinosaurs and their fellow reptiles expressed physical size and ferocity in the Grand Style; bringing it to the highest pitch ever to be achieved on earth: their mission was accomplished. As an achievement of the evolutionary force it is aesthetically satisfying. Neither a failure nor a warning.

At the end of the era of the great reptiles the evolutionary progress, the procession of life, made its sharpest change of direction. Retrospectively this was acknowledged by geologists when they named the succeeding age the Eocene, the dawn of recent life. Our ancestral species were now able to resume their more usual position of a humble rank within the dominant group. For the mammals kept waiting for so long, now hastened to fulfil themselves, to multiply, diversify, and increase in size and strength.

Their surroundings had already a more modern aspect. While the chalk was still forming in clear seas, while the reptiles still enjoyed an undisputed sovereignty, the old vegetation of cycads, ferns, and primitive conifers, which had provided the setting for animal life since the coal forests were overflowed by the sea, gave way before the spread of deciduous trees and flowering plants. Already there were poplars, plane trees, magnolias, and figs. Strange to think that trees very like the planes that make summer for the streets and squares of London and hang out their little strings of seed-balls against her winter skies should have lived in time to be clawed down and eaten by dinosaurs. What an ancient Eden for the fig!

With the coming of the deciduous trees whose young buds and falling leaves at last created the full panoply of the seasonal procession, the rise and fall whose symbolism was to move the heart of man, there came also the first true flowers. Plants at last learnt to hang out bright colours, honey, and pollen to the attentive, necessary bees.

The world man was to inherit, the life that was to be the matrix for his own and the stuff of much of his religion and art were already present on earth seventy-five million years before man himself appeared to recognize and claim them. The properties of mind and imagination were being assembled, but as yet there was no consciousness to give them the reality of a name.

culture 4

The body is completed and culture begun

Many people have been startled to discover that geologists begin their Recent era (the Caenozoic) seventy-five million years ago. This, after all, is not unreasonable when it is remembered (in figures that are conventional, certainly, but not meaningless) that this is some two thousand nine hundred and twenty-five million years after the gaseous birth of this planet and some nine hundred and twenty-five million years after the first stirrings of life upon its surface. Indeed, it is not only not unreasonable but, like a fair proportion of the ideas of scientists, it is altogether reasonable. The Caenozoic epoch was so named because by the beginning of the series of ages comprising it—the Eocene, Oligocene, Miocene, and Pliocene, whose Greek-derived names slip off the tongue, and also out of the memory, as easily as ice-cream—nearly all the creatures that inhabit the world with us today were already in existence or rapidly assuming their present shape.

Seas, lakes, and rivers were stocked with fish whose abundant variety of form and colour included those now familiar from our fishmongers' slabs; shellfish with the flutings, whorls, and corrugations we know were already there together with crustaceans armoured, feelered, and clawed. The insects were in being in their intricate perfection, crawling, hovering, darting, fluttering, buzzing, and stinging. Baltic amber has preserved us butterflies, bees, and ants from this time, its glowing congealed resin perpetuating their brief moments in a way far closer to life even than petrification. Indeed they are exactly comparable to mountaineers and mammoths held in ice. The butterflies already went on emblazoned wings, though perhaps they had not as yet been brought to their present magnificence; spiders had mastered spinning; ants have hardly changed any detail during the last fifty million years, but in their early days had not yet imprisoned themselves within the terrible efficiency of their social life. Birds, the latest of the great orders that eros has created on earth, were only beginning to evolve towards the beauty and variety that we now delight in, but already they flew, waded, dived, and swam, while there also flourished many more great flightless, swift-running species than survive today. In Antarctica there lived penguins as tall as men were in time to be.

As for the mammals, escaping in the Eocene Age from the long and heavy dominance of the reptiles with all the stored exuberance of children bursting out of school, they rather exceeded themselves and many of the most overgrown and grotesquely over-armed of them, monsters like nightmare rhinoceros and hippopotamus, rapidly became extinct. Thinking of them one remembers how one's nurse used to say 'Now don't get over-excited or it will end in tears'. But although there were these excessive species, the foundations of the great mammalian families were already firmly laid. All their main groups were already represented in the Eocene, the marsupials, the rodents, insectivores and carnivores, the ungulates, whales, sea-cows. Also, as I shall soon describe more fully, our own family of the primates. During the succeeding ages there were shaping from these ancestral forms all the creatures that we were at first to hunt and later to preserve and stare at in our zoological gardens and national parks. There were also shaping those animals with which we have entered into very close relationships, approaching dependence. I speak, of course, of the forebears of our cattle, sheep, and pigs, and other domesticated breeds.

From their size, these animals could have furnished the first two voyages of Gulliver. It is well known that horses began the era as little beasts the size of terriers and running on fourteen toes, four on the front feet, three on the hind. Eocene elephants attained about two feet and cattle were much the same lilliputian size. Perhaps it is less familiar knowledge that there were pigs standing as much as six feet in height and exceedingly swift. Had man come into being during Miocene times he must have exploited his fellow creatures in quite different roles from those we have in fact assigned to them. There is nothing very remarkable in the idea of horses and cows stretched on our hearthrugs or elephants drawing lawn-mowers, but I find pleasure in picturing those fashionable sporting events where jockeys galloped on gigantic boars.

At the time when our domestic animals and pets and the surviving wild creatures of earth, air, and land were evolving towards their present bodily forms, the lineaments of our own species were also being drawn. Looking back through the Caenozoic era and watching the emergence of the human form can be likened to watching an imperfect portrait-painter working at study after study, each approaching a little more closely to a true likeness of the sitter. Then, strangely enough, as with the Pleistocene Age we approach the latest phase of the era, man has in fact painted his own portrait and we are looking at the famous L'Angle-sur-l'Anglin head and shoulders of a hunter, the first instance, so far as we have been able to recall, of man's self-consciousness becoming so acute as to enable him to stand apart from himself, form an image of what he saw, and take colour and chisel to render that image in a work of art.

During the immense stretches of earlier epochs we have seen the raw material and roughly shaped parts of our bodies being assembled. The food tracts, backbone, and central nervous system, the tiny budding brain growing as the eyes, ears, and nostrils are perfected; the supporting limbs; the warm bloodstream. Simultaneously we have seen the stuff of our emotions coming into being. Raw pain, fear, and appetite, then thoughtless joy in living and, as the mammals suckled and played with their young, a dawn of that affection, if not yet quite tenderness, that even now with all its human subtlety and sweetness has not outgrown the element of bodily touch, the non-erotic clasp or caress born at this time in the mammalian nest.

The materials assembled, the body now grows up through the Caenozoic towards its present form. Already in the Eocene the shrew-like creatures that had darted after insects among the branches while the giant reptiles pursued their mild or violent ways below them had given rise to the early primates, the first members, that is to say, of the order of mammals to which we ourselves belong. Or rather to which we have assigned ourselves, for it is, of course, only the brain then beginning its expansion that has turned to survey all the creatures of this planet, seemingly without divisions, merging from one kind into another, and has imposed its own divisions upon them. Linnaeus and his like have measured and compared, seen likenesses and dissimilarities and assigned every creature to its species, its genus, its phylum and order, godlike, making order out of chaos. So man has placed himself among the primates, an order he shares with the lemurs, tarsiers, monkeys, and apes.

The first indisputable primates were lemurs, perhaps, like living ones, with furry tails, and enough snout to impede full stereoscopic vision, and the tarsiers, whose huge, forward-staring eyes already saw the world in three dimensions. The diminutive tarsiers, varied and widespread in Eocene and Oligocene times, now survive only in the East Indies, a region extraordinarily distinguished in the history of the primates, still possessing two species of the rare anthropoid apes and having yielded the fossil remains of several varieties of ancient man. Among the early tarsiers, some, it seems, were on the direct line of our ancestry. Indeed, if we handle these springy, highly strung little oddities, whose round eyes have an hypnotic, haunted stare, watch them eat a grape or break up an insect with the deftness of a surgeon, it is not difficult to believe that we are playing with a distant, outmoded kinsman.

Arboreal life encouraged the sense of sight over that of smell, and also the use of the hands for grasping; the diet of fruit, insects, and shoots that accompanied it allowed the retreat of the muzzle necessary to stereoscopic vision and increased the neatness and flexibility of the hands. In time our forebears went beyond running along boughs and leaping from one to another, squirrel-like, and began to use their flexible hands for swinging below the branches—a skill recovered and perfected by the trapeze artists working (without benefit of tail) below the big top.

I see no reason to discredit the popular belief that children's fondness for tree-climbing, to say nothing of the flinging up of arms at the moment of drowning, is an inheritance from the arboreal phase of our history. Certainly my own experience confirms it. I was as a child so passionately fond of climbing in trees as to be secretly convinced of my membership of some tree-dwelling race of beings. I, the daughter of a scientist living in one of the most humdrum and respectably donnish residential roads of Cambridge, spent the greater part of my time out of school in the branches of a large ash tree, using my prehensile hands and bare, but no longer fully prehensile, feet to find a way to every extremity of the tree, sometimes even swinging by my arms from branch to branch—or, as the zoologists would call it, brachiating. When taken to the New Forest on holiday, nothing would keep me on the ground; I lived high among the branches of the beeches, a true denizen, it seemed to me, of their silvery aisles and lofty green tents.

I can still recall my wordless longing to be climbing, and am ready to accept it as just as much an historical recapitulation as the gills and tail I had outgrown in my mother's womb half a dozen years before. At least there can be no doubt at all that our ability to climb, uncommon among animals, was acquired during this remote period of our history and has been kept ever since our ancestors descended from the trees more than thirty million years ago.

When this descent was made our forerunners must have been monkey-like in appearance, but they were not true monkeys, for the family of these entertaining cousins seems to have developed on its own from early in Oligocene times, when one branch made its way into the American continent there to develop broad-nosed species in contrast to the narrow-nosed varieties of the Old World. While it is almost certain that our bodies passed through a monkey-like stage, they also experienced an apish one. This does not mean our forebears ever looked like the brothers and sisters of the modern anthropoid apes, the gorillas, orangutans, and chimpanzees; they did not, but they shared a common ancestry. Consciousness of this kinship draws crowds to their cages in our zoological gardens. We stare at the apes, feeling them to be imprisoned not behind the obvious bars of their cages, but behind a barrier of mind, flimsy, tantalizing but never to be broken down. Anyone who has played with chimpanzees knows how close they are to us in the emotions of affection, pique, anger, and greed, and how through their sense of mischief we can come as near to communication with them as we can with a very young child. We are within hailing distance of fellow individuals yet cannot hope to draw nearer.

The last common ancestor shared by the apes and ourselves (probably living in the Miocene Age, though some anatomists think the parting of our stocks took place even earlier) possessed certain primitive features still to be seen in modern apes which we have lost, but also certain primitive features which we have retained and the apes outgrown. For while simian evolutionary change has been slight and insignificant when compared with our own, it is still considerable. Among the bodily parts in which we are more primitive than our hairy kinsmen the most important are the hand and arm. The hand that we have made supremely skilful is far less specialized, much closer to the five-toed front foot of the amphibians, than is the long, narrow hand of the great apes which has become adapted to their branch-swinging habit. So, too, with our much shorter arms; had we remained for another ten million years or so in the trees the distance involved when a man kept another at arm's length might have been much greater.

The apes have also developed large canine teeth and (particularly the gorillas) a massive bony crest on the top of the head for the attachment of powerful jaw muscles: thus in their hands and arms, in their more rounded heads and smaller teeth, our common ancestors of forty million years ago were more like ourselves than like the existing apes.

During the Miocene Age there took place in Central and South Africa one of those sudden outbursts of evolutionary exuberance within a group of creatures that have been common in biological history. The apes multiplied and diversified, branching out with the vigour of a young plant after rain. Not only did they proliferate into new species, but they spread out from Africa to colonize much of the Old World, until apes were to be seen in many lands where they have now long ago vanished. The Americas they did not penetrate; that continent was to wait until the time less than twenty thousand years ago when men, unknown but in truth greater pioneers than Columbus, could make their way there by raft or boat and find this vast territory supporting no higher form of life than chattering troupes of broad-nosed monkeys.

Men obsessed with the same curiosity, the same desire to recall the long-forgotten events of prehuman history that once took us to Palestine, have of late lifted many fossils of early apes from the caves and river gravels where they had lain for so long in undisturbed oblivion. Now given names—names grown familiar throughout the world—the subject of meticulous study and international argument, these creatures who lived nameless and unself-conscious, still in thoughtless harmony with their surroundings, have suffered a form of rebirth. Parapithecus, Propliopithecus, Proconsul, Pliopithecus, Dryopithecus, an increasing company of creatures that were either among the ancestors of ourselves and of the anthropoid apes or members of extinct collateral lines. It is not yet finally agreed among their learned and scientific descendants just which of these names represent the parental line of the biologically most successful species on earth, now swarming in appalling numbers from the Equator to the poles, and which, on the other hand, represent the diverging simian line of the gibbon, orang, gorilla, and chimpanzee now reduced to a few thousand animals, living hemmed in by the humanly civilized world, remote inhabitants of the tropical forests. Until the beginning of Pleistocene times there can have been very little evidence among the many groups of apes engaged in the endless business of eating and procreating to suggest that they were to reach this parting of the ways—one never to leave the mindless jungle, the other to lead to the wonders, beauties, and abominations of human existence.

Both man and the anthropoid apes are thought to have originated in Africa after the great age of simian evolution which had its centre there. We can feel a satisfactory balancing of history in the fact that the continent, which was later to fall so far behind in the development of human culture that our own grandfathers found some of its peoples still leading the lives of Stone Age hunters, was at this time in the forefront. Africa was the stage for the opening of human history and the first groping attempts to create a culture.

I shall not attempt any further analysis of our simian history. The names of all the principal participants and their relationships with one another, so far as we understand them, will be found in the family tree at the end of this book. Here I want only to write of one group of creatures whose remains, hitherto wholly forgotten, have recently been recovered in considerable numbers. I single out the Australopithecinae of South Africa because they can be recognized as representing the most advanced of the beings that were still more apes than men. Thus they form the essential link with the most ape-like of the true men, represented by the Pithecanthropi of Java and Pekin. These two families symbolize the transition from animal to human kind. Together they help us to recall the fateful time when our precursors began, with a slowness beyond the range of ordinary historical thinking, to raise themselves out of the natural world of unselfconscious life. It is as though from a level ocean there was gradually lifted a waterspout of inestimable force. The power lifting it was the great wind of mental life streaming through the universe.

Australopithecus was a being of about the stature of the surviving pygmy races who (I think it should be who) lived in dry, savannah country, perhaps scattered with trees, and broken with rocky outcrops and scarps where caves and fissures made their dark resistance to the glare of the sun. In these holes in the rock the little men-apes took shelter, probably using them for eating, sleeping, and the rearing of young. They would have been strange, bewildering creatures for a fully evolved man to encounter. They appear to have walked almost upright, carrying their heads balanced upon the spinal column rather than hanging in front of it. Their eyes were set deeply below projecting brows comparable to an ape's, yet behind this bony ridge there sloped a just perceptible forehead, already beginning to plump towards the ripeness of our own high brows. The brain itself, the chief character in the anatomical drama, was in most individuals as small as an ape's, but in a few seems to have reached a size within the human range. The lower part of the face showed the same blending of human with simian features. The jaws projected to form a snout over which the nose must have been flattened and the lips drawn thin, yet the teeth resembled those of man, particularly in the absence of a brutal canine. The palate, too, was broadening towards the back and so approaching the shape of the sounding-board on which men were to produce their words and their singing notes. Australopithecus can have had no true speech, but at times of emotion and excitement he probably expressed himself in cries, a partially controlled gabble, and above all in gestures of the hands and lips.

If in his body he already showed a promise of coming humanity, was this being able to show any manifestation of the birth of culture? There is some evidence, though it is still inconclusive, suggesting that although he did not make tools he may have picked up stones, sticks, or bones to use as clubs and missiles, and possibly used sharp-edged stones for cutting. Thus alike in body and in achievement the Australopithecinae fail to qualify as men, yet in both there is a hint of future powers. Certainly there was every incentive for their growing brain to devise such ways of increasing their physical equipment, for life in the trees had left them with limbs not shaped for speed on the ground, with no great strength and without teeth or claws fit for dispatching or tearing up their prey.

For the Australopithecinae probably could only have survived if they lived at least partly on meat. After the descent from the trees our precursors had evidently abandoned the more delicate vegetarian diet of their arboreal days and taken instead to animal food. The change may have been forced upon them by the spread of a dry, parching climate. Whatever the cause, the result has been to make us at least partial carnivores, yet our bodies had been so far moulded before this change took place that our teeth remain ill-adapted to eating flesh, while our eight yards of intestine were designed for the digestion of vegetable foods.

I find myself wondering if it was a persistent appetite for the varied and delicious flavours of the vegetable kingdom that led (as we shall see) to the remarkably early introduction of cooking. To men with ancestral memories of the subtle range of taste offered by young shoots, by sweet but various fruits and delicate nuts, the tearing of raw meat with inadequate teeth must have been a most monotonous business. A good roast, filling the cave with tantalizing smells, crisping the fat and bringing out the differences between pork, beef, venison, and baboon, would go far towards making good the loss.

I shall choose this point to call attention to one of the most astonishing of all the series of lucky chances in which the orthodox evolutionists ask us to believe. Our forebears had to climb into the branches and adopt an appropriate vegetable diet to be enabled to develop flexible hands, a tendency to hold themselves upright, and stereoscopic vision; they had to climb down again and adopt a meat diet in order to stand on their feet and preserve their hands from the over-specialization they would have suffered had they remained in the trees, and in order to develop tools to make good their deficiencies as hunters and flesh-eaters. Truly a man at the gaming-table would thank Providence if he enjoyed so remarkable a run of good luck.

We have come to regard the division between ourselves and our fellow animals as being so deep and significant as to justify the use of different words for identical things according to whether we are applying them to man or to beast. The little man-ape provides a very wholesome challenge to this assumption. I have already found myself allowing him the pronouns 'he' and 'who'; does he live in a lair or live in a cave dwelling; does he hunt game and have meals or catch his prey and devour its flesh; does he sleep on rough beds or in nests; does he mate or marry and can he be allowed to make love? If we were to shoot him would it be murder or sport? As the viruses help us to see life merging into non-life, so Australopithecus helps us to understand the unity existing between human and animal existence.

This conjunction can be completed by a study of Pithecanthropus, the most brutal-looking of the species that anatomists are willing to allow within the fold of the hominidae or true men. The name Pithecanthropus itself represents a family reunion, for there have now been brought together within this one species several early men whom anatomists once held to be distinct. Most famous among them are Java Man, known as Pithecanthropus erectus, and Pekin Man who was given the name of Sinanthropus pekinensis. Their remains were unearthed thousands of miles apart and with nearly forty years separating the discoveries; furthermore the living individuals who found and studied them belonged to different nationalities. It was these gulfs dividing their recent histories rather than any profound dissimilarity between the men themselves that caused them to be assigned to different species. Had their two races ever come into contact they would very probably have confounded their learned and scientific successors by immediate and successful mating. This probability has now been recognized, and the two estranged varieties of man reunited.

The species appears to have been of Asiatic origin though the stock must have come ultimately from Africa, the accepted home of mankind. Its most ancient known representative is the man whose fossilized bones were taken from the Djetis beds of Java and who was living near the beginning of Pleistocene times. There follow his far more celebrated descendant in Java and the men of the Pekin caves. Meanwhile more advanced collaterals of Pithecanthropus evolved in Africa and spread into Europe; Heidelberg Man, known to his posterity only by a massive lower jaw, was hunting the Neckar valley early in the Pleistocene Age. Probably we can accept Neanderthal Man, the last of the apish types to flourish in Europe, as inheriting much from Pithecanthropic stock, together with Rhodesian Man and other primitive beings who lived on in regions remote from the main centres of human development.

The simian strain was still strong in the Javanese and Pekin men, it showed in the heavy ridge of bone above the brows, the large prominent teeth and absence of chin, probably also in a shambling walk and a head still not fully poised upon the spine. Yet within the clumsy, swinging skull, behind the brutal face the brain was growing both in size and complexity. In fact the Pithecanthropic brain capacity varies widely, but the average of about a thousand cubic centimetres comes well within the human range. The Pithecanthropi have been accepted as human beings, as apemen instead of men-apes, partly for this reason, but partly, and more properly, because in a humble way they were creators, using brain, eye, and hand to shape natural things to their own ends. They were men in their possession of the rudiments of culture.

It is exceedingly difficult, I find, to distinguish to one's own satisfaction between the work of instinct, which in many creatures achieves marvels of ingenuity, and the more elementary works of mind that are regarded as being cultural and something peculiarly our own. Because we are judges in our own case, we may be prejudiced in recognizing the exquisitely made nest of the weaver bird or the beaver's lodge to be the product of blind impersonal forces, while a piece of stone roughly knocked into shape by Pithecanthropus is an altogether different and superior thing, the product of a purposeful mind. We argue that the tools were made deliberately to serve a mentally conceived purpose, that they were improved intelligently as a result of experience and—

unanswerably—that they in fact led on towards true culture and civilization, whereas the nest and the lodge have had no development. Yet taking a longer view through time, we cannot deny that the bird and the rodent must have improved their work, even if when they had achieved a limited efficiency they allowed it to stultify and at last harden into what we call instinct. It has been proved by experiment how some of the activities of birds and animals are reproduced generation after generation even though the young are reared away from their parents, while in the same conditions others are lost. There is, then, profound difference in the innateness of 'instinct' which should make us more cautious in our drawing of boundaries. Life pleasures the understanding by its perfect homogeneity as much as by its infinite and subtle variety.

How can there fail to be unity in the achievement of all life, as there is in its chemical basis? Flowers have evolved their perfection of colour, shape, and scent, insects their brilliance and intricacy of bodily form, birds their plumage and song, animals their strength and grace; man has evolved his noble cultures and his troubled, imperfect soul, nourishing them upon the rest of creation. If, as I believe, evolution has a purpose to achieve in the sense that the acorn is purposeful, then clearly there is an underlying power behind it of which all these manifestations are related parts. In the total picture there can be no absolute division between the feathers put out by a bird-of-paradise and the canvases filled in by painters; all are equally reactions of life expressing itself through the finest organization of matter. I am certainly not inclined to minimize the importance of the human mind and its creative power; for me it is supreme so far as this small planet is concerned; but there is no impassable barrier between it and the rest of existence—as indeed we are proving when, in this book, we find ourselves passing naturally and without question from the changing shape of man's body to the changing shape of his tools and of his cultures.

With Pithecanthropus we have reached the most primitive type of being known to have possessed at least the faint beginnings of a creative culture. The earliest of the breed whose existence we have recalled, the man from the Djetis beds of Java, is not known to have made tools and there is no evidence that his descendant, the more famous Java Man of the Trinil beds, did so. Before Trinil, however, members of the Pithecanthropic stock, the families whose fossilized bones have been recovered from the Choukoutien caves near Pekin, had begun to shape stone into rough choppers and cutting implements. It is significant, however, that they had as yet no standard types of tool, but merely broke and chipped pieces of stone in a haphazard fashion to serve the need of the moment. The deliberate shaping of a fixed type of tool demands the formation of clear mental images. Just as a sculptor must imagine his work of art, creating it mentally before cutting it out from the block, so must the humblest tool-maker see the finished product in his mind's eye before he chips it from the lump of chert or the flint nodule. The Pekin men had not yet established any such mental pattern book, they did not carry about with them images of how certain things should be formed which they could habitually use and then pass on to their children. Yet even their haphazard and sporadic shaping of implements was an achievement. Apes, like Australopithecus, will employ sticks and other objects as tools, but have never been known to shape them. Moreover they possessed other elements of culture that help us to accept these rough creatures as indeed deserving the name of human beings. Among rubbish on the cave floors at Choukoutien—the compact mass of food remains, stone tools and the waste stuff of their manufacture, the skeletons of the men themselves—there were embedded pieces of bright quartz that the hunters had brought from a distant hillside. They had picked them up, perhaps turned them on the leathery skin of their hands enjoying their sparkle in sun or firelight, the simple greed in their deep-set eyes clouded by a questioning wonder. Here surely is the tenuous beginning of our aesthetic pleasure, the use of the senses for contemplation and enjoyment and not only as the instrument of action. Perhaps the beings who collected quartz crystals would also have gathered other pretty things which, being perishable, have been forgotten. Feathers, furs, not impossibly even flowers. They may have used them to ornament their persons, one of those human habits that is as strong in the most primitive as it is in the most exquisitely civilized, a habit which in its mingling of humility, vanity, and self-consciousness comes very close to the bone of human nature.

Also mixed with the cave rubbish were the remains of fires. Pithecanthropus had already learnt to control, if not himself to kindle, the flames of which all animals are afraid. He kept them burning in his cave for protection, warmth, and the roasting of meat. These were the practical uses, but the ring of the firelight must already have inspired feelings of companionableness, however vague and tenuous, within the family group, and a corresponding sense of otherness, of being apart from the dark animal night beyond. So a dim perception of man's selfhood was born. Looking back through half a million years, one can see the lonely hollows of light, here in China and up and down Asia, Africa, and Europe, as though in a painted Nativity; it is true that earth was giving birth to man.

The million years of the Pleistocene Age, which was the last phase of this (by earthly measurement) long-drawn gestation, were marked by violent changes of climate. There were in all four periods during this Age, each lasting from fifty thousand to one hundred and fifty thousand years, when Earth began to freeze. The cause, still disputed among the descendants of the men who ignorantly witnessed the events, was probably some loss in the sun's power. Perhaps if the freezing had gone much further, all higher forms of life would have been annihilated and could hardly have evolved again on this planet. For better for worse, the globe was never wholly frozen, and four times the warmth returned, allowing animals and men to return to the liberated lands. We are now living in the latest of these warm periods, our little Arctic and Antarctic ice-caps, which appear to us to be as normal as the rising of the sun, being in fact the surviving remnants of the Pleistocene glaciations and not normal at all could we look at the history of the planet with less myopic eyes. In this our warm phase (and we cannot tell whether it will grow warmer yet or freeze again) the ice-caps are small and well out of the way, but during the glaciations they vastly extended their range, pushing their fissured, glistening edges southward and northward and thereby shifting the rainbelts towards the Equator to water regions usually arid. At the same time from mountain masses lying towards the poles, glaciers ground down the valleys and spread out over wide tracts of land, smoothing the rocks, spreading thick carpets of clay and gravel and piling up stony moraines. The main pattern of continents and seas into whose intricate shape men were to fit their civilizations was already long established, but the Pleistocene ice added finishing touches to the land surface, modifying it much as a woman modifies her face when she makes her toilet.

This world of pulsating warmth and cold was, then, the setting of man's life during the million years of his final emergence. It saw him grow from a creature capable only of producing the roughest language and tools, the dimmest response to the unusual or beautiful, into a being still uncivilized yet with words on his tongue, many and ingenious tools and weapons in his hands, clothed, ornamented, and able to portray in a brilliant and inspired art the animals among whom he lived. The very inconstancy of the natural surroundings helped to speed this marvellous passage. Changing climate made men adapt their habits, shift their hunting grounds, mingle one kind with another, challenging them to thought and to the realization that the simple cultural forms each several group had created were by no means as universal and inevitable as claws on a bear or an ibex's slender horns.

Yet in spite of the ebb and flow of the ice, and the

corresponding advances and retreats of human life on the face of the earth, cultural growth was slow almost beyond comprehension. To our minds, schooled to a life of galloping technical change and of endless flights of ideas always flickering about the globe, such enormous slowness is oppressive to contemplate. The simple statement of the truth is this: every generation lived like the one before to the extent of hundreds of generations. Yet change there was, and we must suppose it to have been swifter and more purposeful than the weaver birds' improvement of their nests.

The next step beyond the meagre achievement of Pekin Man was the establishment of traditional tool-forms, few in number and little specialized in purpose, yet demanding the presence, in the minds of the men who chipped them, of sure and stable images. Before the second freezing of the earth, different breeds and groups of men were carrying in their brains a modest variety of designs for implements, together with the will-power and co-ordinated control of hand and eye necessary to execute them. Men were rare creatures; probably in any one year of this earlier Pleistocene Age there were no more than some ten thousand brains so equipped. Between them they possessed the mental patterns of sharp tools for penetrating and jointing their prey, of edged tools for cutting them up and scraping their skins, of weighty tools to be used for clubbing, hurling, and the smashing of marrow bones. In time, though we have not yet recalled when, the brains of these hunters came also to imagine the making of traps, a significant advance because setting a trap necessitates a clear sense of the future. All toolmaking, indeed, implies the existence of this sense—a labour is being undertaken for future advantage—but in the idea of a trap it is further advanced, the future is being prepared for in a way that demands the patience and detached imagination of a fully human being.

I will select one tool out of those comprising the repertory of the men of the earlier Old Stone Age and describe its history in some detail, using it to represent much that is of profound interest in the early cultural achievements of our kind. It is the implement which was at once the most widespread, the most precisely formalized, and the best proportioned and executed of its time, the highest product of material culture during the first half of the Pleistocene Age. The hand-axe.

Its beginnings, however, were crude enough. Very early in this age, probably before the first cold phase, men living in Africa began to make tools from rounded pebbles, flaking one end into a rough point. This process, perhaps originally the invention of one man, was long reproduced without further development, but during the course of hundreds of thousands of years and the stress of two ice ages, slowly men devised improvements. They learnt how to chip away the whole of the rough outer cortex of the pebble or nodule, how to make the sides and base regular and sharp enough to give a cutting edge, how to secure a slender point and a balance enabling them to adapt the implement as a club or missile. So, after the rise and fall of some five hundred thousand years and twenty thousand generations, the roughly pointed pebble had become an elegant, pear-shaped tool, made to an identical pattern all the way from India and South Africa to southern England. We can accept the growth of this fine tool as a symbol for the founding of tradition, the necessary basis for all culture. From the first spark of intent, manifest in the occasional and haphazard shaping of stones, there had come a body of purposeful custom and skill. Its improvement was so slow that we can understand how every son and daughter inheriting it from father and mother, largely by watching and imitation rather than by even the simplest precept, assumed in minds still little troubled by thought that their part was to repeat exactly the established forms. Yet the fact that the perfected tool did grow from the pebble shows how even then our species brought forth the exceptional mind which was not content to inherit and transmit tradition but must enrich it. Individuality in those times was faint indeed, but already the gifted individual was making his rare contribution to tradition, the human tradition which, although it has forked into innumerable branches, and, fluctuating in vigour, has allowed some to wither, has been handed on continuously ever since.

It is curious for us to discover in recollecting the earliest history of mankind that the slowness of change, the extreme conservatism of culture, defeated the vastness of space just as does the extreme speed of our communications today. We have seen how our chosen tool was made an identical form over Africa, Asia, and Europe; we are only now beginning to recover so world-wide a culture. Uniformity of interest and products, now spread so quickly by land, sea, and air and through the waves of light and sound, was then carried on the bare feet of hunters who took not merely lifetimes to carry the mental images of culture throughout the continents but many, many generations. Yet change was even slower-footed, and so a simple uniformity was extended throughout most of the Old World.

To me the greatest significance of our tool lies in quite another direction. The best of these implements, deftly flaked from large nodules of flint, have been claimed by some of the descendants of their makers as true works of art. While I prefer to limit this most precious word to creations in which the imagination is expressing emotion and idea, from the point of view of the aesthetics of pure form these flints unquestionably possess an elementary perfection. Yet they were among the first considerable creations of mind to appear on earth. Where did their authors discover this rightness of form, a rightness we still recognize a quarter of a million years later? Did it perhaps, and does it still, spring from memories, deep in the unconscious, of natural forms observed and participated in during the vast stretches of our pre-human evolution? Is it these memories, these inherited prejudices, that make us say: this is right—the relation between this tapering point and this curving butt are so perfectly satisfying as to possess a kind of life of their own? It may be we are moved by such an inheritance, or it may be that as creatures of this world we are swayed by the laws of its construction and existence. I do not know how we come to possess them, but I am sure these aesthetic convictions of ours, these ideas of formal rightness, are bonds between human mind and the universe in which it is lodged. They are also bonds between ourselves and our remote forebears, having passed from brain to brain, from their time until our own, in an unbroken mental process spanning all human history.

We are not quite cut off even from individual makers of our pear-shaped implements. The body of one of them fell in or near a small tributary of the Thames, and some parts of his skeleton, including two bones of the skull, were caught up in its waters and swept along until they came to rest and were buried deep in the gravel bed. There also came to be buried in the same gravels remains of the animals the dead man and his kindred had known and hunted —elephants, deer, rhinoceros—together with some of their flints. These events took place towards the end of the warm phase before earth began to freeze for the third time. During the two hundred thousand summers and winters that have passed over the Thames valley since that day, minerals seeped into the porous bones, including the two skull fragments, and fossilized them. That was all that happened to them. They lay there, secure in their physical existence but without even the possibility of significance while generation after generation of later men passed them by. The last ice age ended, farmers came up the river, then Celts, then Romans; the city of London was built a few miles to the west. Still they had, and could have, no significance. In A.D. 1935 one skull bone was recovered; the second in the following year. The patch of river terrace where they had rested had come to be known as the Swanscombe Pit and they were laid bare by the shovels of men digging gravel for our roads and garden paths.

By now human understanding was ready for the discovery; our minds were able to invest the bones with meaning. Indeed the individual who recognized them was an ardent if humble slave of the compulsive curiosity of our time, of the curiosity which a few years before we had carried to Mount Carmel. He was a dentist who followed his calling not far from the territories where the Stone Age hunters had followed theirs, and for many years his obsession with the past had taken him to neighbouring gravel pits in search of fossil bones. Watching while the quarrymen threw their shovel loads on the riddles, poking round the spoil heaps, he had found the remains of many extinct animals, once inhabitants of the valley. He found the bones of the warmth-loving beasts such as elephant and rhinoceros which were living there when the valley sides were heavy with lush vegetation; he found the remains of the cold-enduring beasts such as mammoth, bison, and lemming which had known it when winds blew off the nearby glaciers, freezing the river and cutting down the vegetation to a dwarfish grey scrub. Then at last the dentist found the pieces of human skull and the ancient hunter was resurrected from his partial grave as Swanscombe Man.

In these two bones modern men were handling the very roof and floor of a brain which had held the image of our pear-shaped tool in its soft folds. They could run their fingers through the small opening in the skull's base where signals once ran to and fro between the brain and the shaping hands, as blow by blow the imagined form was struck from the natural flint.

When the skull of Swanscombe Man was still clothed in flesh, the power of thought being generated on this planet was weak and flickering as a night-light would be in Westminster Hall, but by the time the bones were taken from the gravel pit they were at once exposed to a world-wide glare of scientific thought and speculation. They became the centre of disputes, they caused both glory and pain and humiliation such as their living owner could never have known. The hazards of triumph or of failure in hunting elephant and rhinoceros would be mild indeed when compared with those to which modern man is exposed in the pursuit of science and learning.

The significance for us of Swanscombe Man has, however, been firmly established. Measurement, restoration, and comparison of his occipital and parietal bones have shown that his head was quite remarkably like those of the measurers, restorers, and comparers—and indeed of all the rest of us alive today. It proved possible to set up the left side of the ancient hunter's head against a right-hand side taken from modern man and secure perfect symmetry of outline, the only difference being the much greater thickness of the bony vault in Swanscombe Man. The size of the brain and its convolutions had been like ours; no facial bones survive, but although the features may have been rather heavy there is no reason to think this face would have caused any surprise had one passed it on the pavement of London or New York.

So now at last in our scrutiny of the past we come unmistakably face to face with ourselves. The story of our emerging bodies which we have followed from the little wriggling fish-like creatures of the Silurian waters, adding part to part through the passing ages, has reached its end. Among the abundant animal life of the Thames valley in mid-Pleistocene times men of our own kind went their way already fully equipped in head, heart, and hands to achieve what we their descendants have achieved. Had some demiurge chosen to take a fer-

Securing the spoken word which, until then, had drifted into oblivion

PHARAOH AKHENATEN

The first individual in history?

tilized ovum from Swanscombe Woman and set it in some twentieth-century womb, I think it very likely that a human being would have been born quite able to grow up into the modern world, even if the furniture of his unconscious mind might differ from our own.

Although we have encountered the earliest certain member of our own kind living in Britain between the second and third glaciation, it seems that our stock first evolved long before, and in Africa. The dark continent had nourished the first humans, and then it is thought the first men of modern kind; certainly it saw the shaping of the pointed pebbles which are the oldest known intelligently shaped tools on earth, and which, subsequently, in the hands of Homo sapiens developed the perfection we have seen.

Ideally the line of our descent is from Australopithecus through Pithecanthropus to Swanscombe Man, but historically the story is far less direct. In fact men very much like ourselves were probably living in Africa even before the ape-men made their home in the caves of Choukoutien. Unquestionably the two races, one simian, the other of the breed in time to call itself sapient, shared the land surfaces of the planet through the second half of Pleistocene times. Our own direct ancestors, originating in a warm climate, appear always to have retreated before the advancing cold of the glacial phases. Just as the onset of the northern winter was later to make the more tender among the English migrate to the Mediterranean and New Englanders towards their own southern sun, so it seems their ancestors moved southwards, to Africa and India, before the seemingly eternal winters of the Pleistocene. The more apish men, on the other hand, much tougher and perhaps protected by a hairy pelt of their own as well as by animal furs, like the less tender or fortunate Englishman, remained to face the cold.

The two breeds, then, tended to occupy different territories, but often they came into contact, feeling presumably as alien to one another as white man and Negro at their first encounters. They were even more dissimilar in their bodily parts, but in cultural attainments were for long much closer together. Indeed, in the cultural exchange that in time began to take place between them, Homo sapiens evidently took almost as much as he gave; that, at least, is how we read the stone tools left in gravels, drifts, and cave floors, the only means we have of recalling these remote but profoundly important happenings.

As the last freezing of the earth crawled towards its harsh climax some fifty thousand years ago, the physical contrast between the two instead of lessening became more conspicuous than before. At that time a vast region from Britain at least as far eastwards as Palestine and from Siberia to North Africa was inhabited by the Neanderthal men who seem to have been caught up in a regressive biological current and carried backwards towards a more brutal anatomy than that of their own forebears. They had in an extreme form the heavy ridges of bone above the eyes seen in Pithecanthropus, with broad flattened nose, prominent teeth, and massive but chinless jaw. They were normally about five feet in height, but carried the head forward on a very thick neck and walked with a stoop and a shambling gait, being in their limbs and in the carriage of the head more simian than the Pekin men of something like two hundred thousand years before. It might be supposed that the Neanderthal race was an offshoot from Pithecanthropus that had survived in some remote region, perhaps in cold forest surroundings, and had been enabled by a tough physique to spread and conquer during the last ice age, were it not for one thing. Though their foreheads were low and the vault of their skulls depressed like the top of a bun, their brains were large, rather larger than the normal size for modern man. Thus it seems they must have been in the main stream of evolution towards Homo sapiens, but were then caught in an eddy and carried back towards apishness, more helpless, if that is possible, than we are today in the destructive torrent of our lunatic technology.

This capacious brain makes it less surprising that being so thick and clumsy these men should yet be skilful in the shaping of flint. They had little ingenuity, for their tools were nearly all designed for skinning and jointing beasts killed in the hunt and for preparing pelts; they had no very specialized implements and seem never to have learnt to work bone. But the limited range of tools familiar to them they made well, giving them a strong, clear-cut form and a neat finish. They were also brave and successful hunters, bringing down such great game as mammoth and rhinoceros.

It is for us significant and oddly touching to find Neanderthal Man suffering, so it seems, from some stirring of a spiritual sense—a consciousness however faint of mind and will and individuality, a notion that these things might have an existence of their own. Collections of bears' skulls hidden in caves may be memories of magic, of a faith in the power of mind and will to work beyond the reach of the hands. Again, while we are no longer inclined to allow a high spiritual value to cannibalism, when it is practised as Neanderthal Man practised it, not for mere hunger or gourmandism but ritually, it implies a belief in super-physical qualities, such as bravery, strength, cunning, or power, which one individual could win from another through a communion meal. Most poignant of all, the careful burial of a corpse near the hearth and the provision of food for the dead man suggests that these poor creatures, already almost on their way out of this world, were to take immortal longings with them.

To me it appears significant that a species which was so different from our own and had fallen so far short of ours as to be doomed to extinction, had nevertheless acquired not only skill and cunning but also intuitions of the life of mind and spirit. Surely evolving life was aiming to put out the sacred fruits of mind if it set them budding in many species—species that were near misses, falling short of the human goal?

The slow, silent, unrecorded clash between the last of the ape-men and our ancestors happened during the last ice age—in Europe mainly during the slightly warmer interlude breaking the climax of that final glaciation. The two stocks had long been on a near equality in their material culture; although in such creations as our pear-shaped tool the early representatives of Homo sapiens had shown themselves perhaps a little more enterprising, a little more gifted in their feelings for pure form, they had not been on an altogether higher level of attainment as Europeans were when they entered Africa and the Pacific. Now, however, they made a relatively rapid advance. From a state of affairs where a few traditional images were handed on down the generations and improvements were rare, slight and sporadic, now in the last phase of the Old Stone Age they become frequent and deliberately directed. The implements they made give the impression of mind purposefully engaged in satisfying needs, in seeking to make new inventions. In place of the few traditional kinds of tool and weapon these men were soon to make a rich variety, each for a clear and limited purpose. They invented new methods for obtaining long blades of flint; they learnt how to work bone and antler and designed stone tools for the purpose; in time they even learnt how to make use of mechanical principles, inventing first the spear-thrower and then the bow and arrow. This was not only the first time on earth that mechanics had been brought by mind to aid animal muscles, but the beginning of man's career as a winger of death over great distances.

While men were using their hands with increasing ingenuity to shape material things they must also have been using their wills to shape society. There probably grew up among them at this time such social intricacies as age grades, secret societies, totemistic groupings, control by chiefs, elders, and medicine men. With these things would have gone the imposition of strict sexual rules; in place of casual mating, including, one must suppose, sexual relations between members of a family, societies were now establishing prohibitions, decreeing that young men should choose brides here and not there—and above all not from the immediate family group. Whence came this will which caused men to force upon themselves all manner of obstacles to the satisfaction of the desires which, like their bodies, they had inherited from the vast eras of their natural history? Here was a species descended from sportive and lustful apes, living in a world where creatures of every sort from the gilded fly to the mammoth coupled freely, without let or care, which yet imposed upon its members rules always a little too cruelly hard for them to obey. Whatever the source of this collective will, it imposed its restrictions and men soon accepted them as given by gods or spirits; incest became an enormity, and the sexes increasingly divided, with the result that sex itself became an increasingly exciting and conscious activity. (The penis might be decorated, and if woman was still usually taken from behind, the more intimate and personal face-to-face position was already known.) Energy and emotion were confined and stored and therefore heightened in force for the creation of culture.

In describing this sudden acceleration in human achievement that makes the end of the Old Stone Age one of the most important ages in our history, I have advanced rather too far in time. Some of these things were accomplished only after Homo sapiens had exterminated the last of the ape-men and had the Old World in his possession. We shall never be able to recall how this extermination of the Neanderthal species was accomplished. In some parts of Asia and Africa where Homo sapiens had not made so dramatic a cultural advance, yet had sufficient superiority of brain power still to prevail, the process may have been gradual and mild. Perhaps in these territories the ape-men may have been pushed into diminishing and impoverished hunting-grounds and been picked off whenever they tried to stray beyond them. Perhaps, too, as has happened with many kinds of wild animals, these humans had some inner conviction of defeat which undermined the will to live, until infertility rather than their enemies caused their final extinction.

In Europe, where our curiosity has recovered more understanding of these events than any other part of the world, it seems likely that the encounter between man and ape-man was sharper and more quickly decided. Our ancestors had made their great cultural advances in some region either of eastern Europe or south-west Asia, so that when they pushed across Europe their equipment and their social organization were good enough to make the Neanderthal men their helpless victims. By the time the final ice age had worsened again after the warm spell we find the ape-men supplanted, their hunting-grounds taken over, and their cave dwellings now sheltering the conquerors.

Throughout the world the Neanderthal stock vanished as though its hour had struck at some icy midnight; only a few stragglers survived for a while in remote corners of the continents. One such survivor was the Rhodesian Man whose unmistakably brutish skull was unearthed by the lead miners of Broken Hill.

One wonders whether the Cro-Magnon men in their encounters with this lowly race felt the scorn and arrogant superiority which until recently white men have felt for primitive native peoples. Were they conscious enough of their own humanity to regard them as sub-human, perhaps as animals? Did they hunt them, sending their fleet, bone-tipped spears after their terrified victims whose own weapons were hopelessly outdistanced. Laughing at their stupidity, did they lure them into traps or pen them in their caves and carry off the women and children as slaves or beasts of burden? We can be sure they were cruel and that the ape-men, mastered by their intelligence, believed themselves to be enmeshed in a powerful and all-pervading magic. However merciless they may have been, these men were more innocent than their descendants who thousands of years later again came into contact with peoples culturally at their mercy—those peoples who in the belief that they alone had knowledge of God dared to think it better for the primitives to die, baptized, in the stinking holds of slave ships than to live as heathen in their own lands. Civilized man's acceptance of brotherhood with primitive peoples is surely one of the most real advances made by our kind in recent times.

It was probably during this time that the foundations of race were laid and these future conflicts made inevitable. The men who extinguished the Neanderthal species were by no means all alike. Cro-Magnon Man was very much of the present west and north European type, but the individual whose remains were found at Grimaldi has been likened to a Negro and Chancelade Man to an esquimau. These identifications should not be taken over-seriously, but there is no doubt that already by the end of the Old Stone Age there was wide diversity in the spreading species of Homo sapiens. During the succeeding Middle Stone Age, when changes of climate and the growth of great forest barriers hindered the movement of peoples, confining them to homelands where the racial distinctions could harden and clarify, there must have emerged a pattern of world races quite close to that of today.

We have to imagine, then, those skins of black and brown, whitish and yellow, those narrow or full and prominent lips, those noses ranging from flat to beaky and tresses from smooth and pale to frizzy and black, becoming more and more sharply distinguished as men bred generation after generation within their territories. It cannot be told from what long roots in the past these differences sprang; it may well be that unmistakably primitive races such as the Tasmanian and Australian had a relatively large inheritance from the old Pithecanthropic stock.

Once the racial trends had begun, the interplay of historical events and adaptation to the lands in which they lived shaped Nordic and Mongol, Mediterranean and Negro, Polynesian and Australian, all the dramatically variegated medley of peoples composing the human species. Even without the embellishments devised by our restless and ingenious minds, the top hats and turbans, the nose plugs and watch chains, feather cloaks, togas and Ulsters, loin cloths and armour, we are naturally the most diverse species on earth. Wild birds and animals lose the ability to interbreed when they have diverged far less conspicuously than has a Bushman from a Swede. Only dogs, cats, and other domestic breeds subject to our own will and fancy have so wide a liberty of form. Indeed, it is not necessary to go to Crufts to see that the dogs have far outstripped their masters in elegant variation.

So it can be assumed that by the end of the hunting epoch on earth the racial pattern had been roughly established, leaving us an inheritance which we may curse for the hatred and cruelty it has aroused, for the terrible problems with which it even now confronts us, or bless for the rich cultural variety, the pride and high achievement which it has fostered. Without race we might be more peaceful but very much poorer.

I have written, glibly enough, of the acceleration in human achievement in the last phase of the Old Stone Age; I have spoken of a sudden technical advance and of the dawn of a sense of endeavour and directed improvement breaking in upon man's million-year-old conservatism. All this is so true that we have to recognize this as the first of the great creative epochs in human history which, at increasingly short intervals, have driven us onward, for better for worse, with the explosive force of a jet engine.

What lay behind this first acceleration? Men endowed with the physical equipment needed for the attainment of full human stature had, it seems, been living on this planet for hundreds of thousands of years, yet had failed to be much more creative than the apemen. Plainly the rapid progress in material culture followed the flowering of some mental quality. We in our curiosity, seeking for memories of these crucial days among the bones and stones, believe that it was language which then flowered.

During the evolution of life on earth, sounds one after another had come into being. Perhaps the fish send sound waves through the Devonian waters as they are reported to shriek and bellow in the deep seas, but the first vocal sound on land was the croaking of amphibians, followed by whatever range of harsh and horrid calls was possible to the giant reptiles. The tree-shrews probably squeaked and their successors among the primates chattered and spat, while round them by now was sounding the vast, bizarre orchestra of the wild life on earth, its howls, barks, whistles, and roars and, among them, the mysteriously composed music of the birds. Most of these utterances expressed love, hunger, anger, fear, and pain. They began, became formalized and constant in their variety; we can still, if we will, hear most of them, each proper to its creature, and each creature to its land.

As these calls and cries became stabilized the human voice still had much further to go. If Australopithecus and Pithecanthropus jabbered, gesticulated, and mouthed with enough precision to suggest states of feeling and even acts, their descendants could probably so frame the waves of sound with tongue and lips, teeth and palate as to be able to distinguish between a number of states and activities. 'Shall-hunt. Shall-fish. Am-hungry. Am-cold. Tool-finished.' If sound could be accurately enough shaped to express such things, then words had at last come into the world, but they were still loose, incapable of objectivity and the labelling of particular things—all remained too much a part of the totality of experience. No one could say: 'This is a bison, that is a mammoth. The cave is cold, the fire has gone out.' It is just these advances, then, that may have been accomplished by Homo sapiens during the last ice age. Once made, the further elaboration of vocabulary and construction was easy; as soon as it could be asked: 'What went wrong with my spear yesterday? How can I make a better one now?' a sudden, purposeful acceleration in cultural achievement became possible. Probably for long there would be no generalizations or collective words, still less abstract ones. There would be mammoth, bison, horse, and reindeer but not animal: there would be Tom, Dick, and Harry but not man. Still, among the inarticulate utterances of animal life the sound of human language had begun, the sound that was to swell, to become more diverse, more subtle as it echoed through time from that day to this. Language that was to give an outline to old shapeless feelings; the vehicle for thought, the stuff of poetry.

This is not an explanation of what happened to our kind at this most important moment of history, it is merely pushing the cause one remove further back. One can well ask how it was that a few thousand beings living in the depths of the primeval world, the abounding, thoughtless world of nature, evolved the intricacies of brain construction that proved equal to formulating language and quite soon to creating the thought, emotions, sensibilities, and skills of such geniuses as Socrates, Shakespeare, Rembrandt, Newton, and Beethoven. That natural selection alone produced the mechanism for writing *Hamlet* and the last Quartets, I find myself unable to believe.

The presence of another force behind the evolution of the human brain, something greater than the life force in a few tribes of savages, is immediately suggested by an astonishing flowering of genius which took place at this very time, thousands of years before the building of civilization. Some of the tribes, the Cro-Magnons and others, who occupied Europe at the end of Pleistocene times have become famous among us as the creators of a great artistic movement, by some twenty thousand years the earliest art in the world. It has always appeared to me to be the most astonishing and improbable event in the whole of human history. Imagine these hunters! Behind them a vast span of animal forebears and a million years of dark, persistent savagery; round them the grim tundra and grassland of a sub-arctic continent.

Suddenly out of this wilderness and the brain and being of man there sprang a noble art. We claim original genius for men and women who set out along well-worn tracks of human experience and take but one step further into the unknown. These early Europeans in a world where, quite simply, there had never been art, took manganese and haematite and ochre, bone and stone, antler and ivory, devised brushes and chisels and painted, carved, engraved and modelled superb portraits of the wild beasts among which they found thmeselves. This is an originality unequalled and almost beyond understanding. It is as though a beggar wandered into a desert by night and returned bearing pearls, wine, and a lighted lamp.

At first, it is true, the pictures were often simple outlines or silhouettes, but there was no bungling or hesitancy in them and before long they were manifesting every subtlety of shading and foreshortening in a brilliant impressionism. They caught the force and malice of the bison and the fragility of the deer, the ferocity of boars, the sturdy ordinariness of wild ponies, and the mammoth's slight absurdity.

Here they were, all the species of animals whose bodies had been shaping side by side with man's, growing with him through time, now suddenly set apart from him, observed, imagined, fixed in pigment on the cave wall. So at Altamira, Font-de-Gaume, L'Angle-sur-l'Anglin, and a score of other caves penetrated during the last half-century, but beyond all at Lascaux, we find ourselves among these beasts, turning upon them eyes that belong to the other end of history, heavy with the knowledge of five millennia of civilized art. The swellings and hollows of the limestone fold one in their cloudy, dreamlike world. On every hand and overhead the forms of horned cattle, horses, deer, and gigantic bulls run, leap, or stand waiting. They have been there so long in the darkness guarding the movement and life, the poetic intensity, with which the Stone Age artists embued them. Now they live again. Some of the species portrayed have become extinct, their world vanished with the melting ice, yet art did what it was always to do afterwards, it cheated time a little, allowing us to re-experience something of a strange and ancient emotion.

Even so it is difficult for us to return to their vision. There have been modern writers on Stone Age art who have argued as to whether it was produced solely for magical purposes or whether it was art for art's sake; there have been writers who argued that cave painting began by outlining shadows, others who said the artists made their studies from the dead bodies of animals killed in the chase. These notions I believe to be entirely misleading and to issue on the one hand from a failure to imagine the unity of all experience for these hunters, and on the other a total ignorance, only possible to men of the Machine Age, of the modes of artistic creation.

His skills, the defining power of language, a heightening of aesthetic enjoyment, all these aspects of experience were strengthening man's consciousness of himself and therefore of a barrier rising between himself and nature. But within that consciousness experience was still without barriers. These hunters had little sense of individual personal life; every man and woman was sunk deeply into the tribe, and not only into the living tribe but all its dead ancestors and descendants yet unborn: there was unity between past, present, and future, natural and supernatural, image and physical reality.

Man, then, felt himself apart from his fellow animals, but he admired, venerated, their physical perfection, intuitively perceiving how it contrasted with the tormenting imperfections of his dawning mental life. Many hunting peoples apologize to the animals they kill, asking their forgiveness, propitiating them. The Stone Age hunters spent their days in seeking, following, and drawing near to wild animals; the moment of the kill gave them their most intense excitement; touching the dead or dying body exercised a different emotion. Here in the game animals was the source of their food, clothes, and of many of their tools; lay the object of ambition, the means of winning status within the tribe.

So these men, feeling their difference from the beasts, yet with these beasts occupying all their days and most of their desires, sought to re-identify themselves with them through communion. They dressed themselves in their skins, horns, antlers, they ate ritual feasts, probably they imagined common spirit ancestors that made them one flesh with a totemic animal. They went into caves, sometimes far into the rock, and there made images of the animals, their work being, as all art was to be afterwards, another attempt at communion, at the recovery of unity with all existence. There was no question here of copying shadows or dead bodies; the emotionally charged mental images produced these paintings so brilliantly expressive of the essential nature of each species. I am reminded of a gifted child who, having been taken into lovely country and set before his easel to paint it, drew instead a London toyshop which was filling his imagination. It may be that the closed-in cave, cutting the artists off from the familiar world of action, helped them to visualize their images; certainly it well symbolizes the inner life of man that was then beginning.

The other focus of emotion and desire was in sex, now sharpened by restrictions beginning to have the name and force of a sanctioned morality. Thus among the vast numbers of portraits of animals there are a few carvings of women, always wide-hipped, big-bellied, and with full breasts. In one cave the woman, a dignified, utterly impersonal figure, sits holding a horn; in another there are three female bodies, carved among those of bison, horses, and ibex, the inessential heads and feet missing but the sexual organs emphasized. Far beyond the range of the painted caves, other tribes of this age carved female statuettes, again full-curved and pregnant, and occasionally inspired with great dignity and grace, as lovely as any images of the Great Mother to be made in the long history lying before her.

For it seems that although the ability to shape these figures came from the emotional excitement the artist experienced in his sexual life, they were images in some cult of fertility which probably included both men and beasts. It is a truly astonishing thing to find the first of the world's artists already portraying the goddess of the feminine principle, who was to be worshipped under so many names by their still distant successors, the Sumerians, Egyptians, Greeks, Romans, and Roman Catholics. Here, long before agriculture turned her into an Earth Mother, and before men were ready to personify her under an individual name—T'iamaat, Juno, Mary—here was the image of this principle, passive, continuing, abundant: the sea, the earth, flesh, fertility, woman. Here is the oldest symbol of all those we have created.

In only one cave of them all has our new curiosity found a lifelike portrait of a man. This was at L'Angle-sur-l'Anglin, the sanctuary of the three female figures; perhaps in a place so heavy with femininity man became sufficiently conscious of his male otherness to be able to see himself as an object. There he is, a head and shoulders, carved in low relief in the limestone, then painted, and touched up with fine engraving. He has thick black hair and beard, a heavy sunken nose and rather prominent teeth, ruddy cheeks and eyes in which the pigments glint a deep blue. He is protected against the cold, now seeming more alien than the man himself in this sunny valley of the Vienne, by a high fur cape or collar sufficiently open in front to show a red undergarment. It is not a fine work of art; probably both intensity of feeling and traditional technique were equally lacking in the artist tackling this unusual subject. Nor is it a remarkable face—it might represent a Shakespearian actor in one of the hairier kinds of provincial production. Nevertheless the promised, historic moment has come. We have watched the human body and countenance taking shape amidst the flowing sap and blood of nature; we have seen the form we ourselves inherit emerge while more brutal versions foundered. We have seen consciousness heightening, cutting off this bewildered man from his surroundings. And now in a little limestone valley of western Europe man sees what has emerged, sees and imagines himself and expresses the image in paint and stone so that we can return and renew his vision. Oddly enough it was a woman, the very woman who led us to Palestine, who unearthed the portrait, and thereby recalled the ancient hunter to our memory.

Beneath the black hair of the man's head was the skull we have seen rising like a bubble gently blown, as inside it the brain has swelled, become more subtly convoluted, more developed in the foreparts lying behind the brow and enclosed in a cortex of grey matter not possessed by other animals. This pulpy mass, so easily spilled, is the mechanism that is about to bring civilization into being, the mechanism that is to control the planet which brought it forth and to create a new world of its own.

Whether we believe this instrument to have been shaped by a series of chances—the chances that kindled life, brought the amphibians out of the water, took the shrews into the trees, equipped them well for arboreal life and a vegetarian diet, carried them down on to the ground again badly equipped for a carnivorous diet, necessitated their making tools, talking, painting portraits of animals, of themselves —whether we believe in these chances, or, on the contrary, hold the growth of brain as an instrument of consciousness to have been part of some more general unfolding, and its achievements to be in harmony, though feebly and from far off, with higher levels of being within the universe, the truth remains the same, that this stuff in its oval casket of bone represents the height of creative power on earth and the place where mind is most obviously immanent in living matter.

During the last few years our brains have been turning to study themselves in minute detail, and although they have come no nearer understanding the central mystery, although as Sir Charles Sherrington's own admirable brain has enabled him to say: 'Aristotle, 2,000 years ago, was asking how is the mind attached to the body. We are asking that question still', they have gained considerable knowledge of their history and functional anatomy. Also, perhaps, they are learning to avoid the dualism implicit in all statements which, like Sir Charles', seem to treat the mind as a detachable entity. My own headpiece tells me to devote the next chapter to an account of the human brain as a logical prelude to the appearance of civilization. For civilization sprang from the convoluted hemispheres contained in a few thousand skulls as surely as a lily from its corm.

brain 5

The meeting-place of body and culture

The human brain is about eight inches long, six inches across, four inches deep, and three pounds in weight. It contains some ten thousand million nerve cells, about four times as many as there are at present men on earth. It rests on a rough, bony floor and is vaulted over with four or five smooth, gracefully curved bone plates held together by sutures far more intricately cut than the finest jigsaw puzzle. I have said four or five, not because I am too lazy to look up the correct number, but because the plate forming the forehead is in two parts in infancy, but normally fuses into one bone in later life. Occasionally, however, an adult may retain a suture right down the middle of his forehead.

Now that we have long known our consciousness to be enthroned in the brain, we seem almost able to feel our thoughts stirring within our skulls. We should remind ourselves how Aristotle, generally held to be an able and observant man, chose the heart as the organ of mind, supposing the soft, convoluted mass within the skull to be a cooling place for the blood. It took many ages for the mind to discover its own centre.

It would be utterly misleading to regard the brain and its indigenous mind in isolation from the rest of our being. Every part of the body contributes to the quality of its work, particularly the senses which are brain's indispensable minions. Deficiency in the thyroid gland, situated in the neck, turns a man into an idiot, while Carlyle is an example of many in whom the whole nature of a man's thought is affected by dyspepsia. We all know men and women whose imaginative faculties have failed to develop through a starvation of the sexual and general emotional life. Indeed I have myself experienced it from within. When at the age of nearly thirty I fell violently in love for the first time a whole new realm of consciousness came into being with overwhelming suddenness, as though someone had pressed the switch in a dark room. Everything my eyes rested upon was full of a new beauty, and in the poetry on which I feasted the images seemed to dance and flame with life. It would be folly to hail the brain as the absolute and independent sovereign either of the individual or of all mankind; yet because it is the instrument of thought, the dwelling-place of consciousness, it does in a very special way incorporate the essence of our humanity. Although the union of mind and matter remains mysterious, we have discovered the brain to be their central power-station. So it can legitimately be used in this book to symbolize the link between the bodily evolution of our kind and the history of civilization.

The brain's anatomy closely reproduces its own past history: that is its greatest fascination. One can say: 'So does the entire body; there is no part of us which is not the creation of time.' True, yet the historical nature of the structure within the skull is more dramatic, for here the ancient parts survive in almost their original form and the new have been added to them, as in a Gothic cathedral with a Norman nave, Decorated choir, and Perpendicular aisles and transepts. Thus with peculiar vividness it shows how life defeats time, its present moment always embracing the past's whole achievement. The embryo repeats in rough summary the events of hundreds of millions of years in nine months, but the brain maintains them all simultaneously. Our past life from worms through fishes and amphibians towards mammals is summed up in the Old Brain, while the advance towards full humanity is expressed in the elaboration of the New Brain, these convoluted hemispheres that dwarf and all but conceal their primitive antecedents.

In an earlier chapter I have described how the spinal cord of a creature resembling the little mud-lurking lancelet was the beginning of the Central Nervous System and how, as that system acquired more duties in controlling the bodily movement and servicing the senses, the upper end of the spinal cord developed the nobby ganglion that was the beginning of brain. By the time of the fishes this had become a true if elementary brain, duly housed in a protective skull; among the amphibians with four jointed limbs and a head to be moved and rapidly sharpening terrestrial senses, it extended further forward again within a skull now massive and sharply defined. It is to be expected, then, that in man the portion of the brain lying where the spinal cord leaves the flexible tunnel of the vertebrae and passes through the neat hole left open for it in the floor of the skull should be the most primitive. Here are the Medulla and Pons, survivals from the worm stage of our ancestry, while the Cerebellum, hanging a little below, was present already in the fishy phase. Above the Pons lie the four nobs of the Corpora Quadrigemina, developed by the amphibians, and beyond and below them the Thalamus, the last and largest department of the Old Brain that underlies the New Brain and was also present already in the amphibians. The Thalamus and its lower extension, the Hypothalamus, have intimate connections with the ganglia forming the terminals of the nerves serving all the vital internal organs of the body, including the sexual organs, and also with the nerves of the eyes and nose and ears, the only major nerves which do not also pass through the primitive centres of the Medulla and Pons. Growing from the Thalamus but extending over the whole Old Brain like some crinkled mob cap is the New Brain, the Cerebrum or

Cerebral Cortex, which, from tiny beginnings in the more evolved amphibians, was enlarged in the mammals and then in the primates, but has attained its overwhelming size and importance only in man. Surrounding all these parts, both externally and within their central cavities, flows the cerebro-spinal fluid which also bathes the half-yard of the spinal cord.

This, then, is the anatomy and chronology of the human brain, the most subtle and intricate instrument on earth. An ingenious scientist has calculated that if it were to be reproduced with components like those of the 'mechanical brains' already in use among us, it would demand several million cubic feet of storage space, and cost well over £1,000,000,000,000,000,000 to build and some even more astronomical figure to run. It would still, of course, lack many of the true mental qualities of the human brain, which can be stored in a space of eight inches by six, and costs at the most some £5,000 to build and train.

Mention of mechanical brains reminds me that before going on to describe something of the functions of the brain components I should warn myself against the many traps waiting for those who write about this subject. It is so easy to talk of the physical brain and its functions as though they were a mechanical mind and as though they were the cause of mind, instead of being the instrument in which, mysteriously, mind is always at work. It is a little as though a strange being finding a copy of *Anna Karenina* and discovering the purpose and meaning of letters and written words, came to suppose that the book had caused the story, instead of being the mere mechanical fixing of Tolstoy's imagination. On the other hand if we think too far on these lines there is an equally great danger of falling into a false dualism, like Descartes, who saw mind as a distinct element, working through the Pineal Eye (of all organs—that anomalous relic of most primitive life) and using the brain as a machine to carry out its purposes. Whether one believes, as I do, that our evolution has been part of a purposeful force driving towards mental consciousness, or whether, like the orthodox biologist, one believes consciousness to have been brought into being by the chances of natural selection, we have to accept mind as being a quality of life as heat is of fire. Even if with super-human intelligence one steers between the Scylla and Charybdis of the traps of mechanism and dualism, there remains the danger of altogether overlooking poor John Smith, so agonizingly aware of the brevity of his span of consciousness and surely right in his belief that he is more than a mere carrying device for the processes of mind.

I am bound to flounder in the coming pages, for not only, as I have just reminded myself, is it beset with fiendishly cunning traps, but also is in a curious way shocking or even painful, so that one turns to it reluctantly. Young ladies brought up in the prudery of nineteenth-century England used to suffer from a shock of shame if they caught sight of their naked bodies in the glass; it seems the mind has some such scruples about looking nakedly at itself. However, the time has come to study the functions of those different parts of the brain, accumulated over so vast a stretch of time. The chronological plan of the structure naturally influences its functions. Thus as the brain steadily pushed forward from Medulla to

Pons, and so on ultimately to Cerebrum so, inevitably, the higher functions of consciousness moved forward. While in the humbler animals some degree of consciousness is centred in the part of the brain represented by the Corpora Quadrigemina, in man this old centre cannot be said to play any direct part in conscious life. At the same time this advancing of the front line of consciousness has also meant that all the nervous connections of the body must pass through the primitive brain centres before reaching the high ones, so that the New Brain can never lose touch with its forebears. The survival of these primitive centres as working parts of the whole relieves the Cerebrum of many banausic duties of plain living, leaving it relatively free to be occupied with high thinking.

Day and night the most ancient part of the brain, the Medulla and Pons, is at work incognito regulating the affairs of the body, the working of its myriad constituents. So long as it is intact the lungs will breathe and the heart beat even though the conscious mind is out of action from sleep, shock, or anaesthetics. The Cerebellum, working in conjunction with the coiled tubes of the semicircular Canals set inside the ear, is principally concerned with the balance and posture of the body and its movements through space. In man it is relatively small, showing like a little chignon below the mass of the Cerebrum, but in birds, as one might suppose, it is a large and highly important part of the brain. The Corpora Quadrigemina, once the seat of such consciousness as there was in the world, serves an obscure purpose in the human brain, being directly responsible only for such minor duties as the contraction of the pupils of the eye.

The Thalamus and Hypothalamus, although part of the Old Brain, play a role of the greatest importance in our conscious lives. They serve as a kind of intermediary between the unconscious life of the body and the Cerebrum, the prime seat of consciousness. Little known in the world, hidden out of sight below the enveloping folds of the Cerebrum, the Thalamus has yet been recognized as 'the power behind the throne of human nature'. It is above all concerned with feeling, with the great, all-pervading emotions of anger, fear, and pleasure and so with giving the individual his sense of the tone and colour of life. While all the lower brain centres are standardized and vary little between man and man, the Thalamus is already highly individual, and indeed appears to inspire all the deeper levels of personality, those mysterious qualities we may call weight or density, which are so universally apprehended yet which remain so difficult to define in words. The thalamic brain is feminine in its nature, in contrast with the essential masculinity of the Cerebrum, or, in the old phrase, it represents heart as opposed to head. Here, in this dark, 'hidden chamber' surely lies the belly with which D. H. Lawrence would have us think. A Cerebrum so overdeveloped as to inhibit the Thalamus underlies that brittleness, silliness, and lack of true feeling characteristic of the pure 'intellectual', whom we expect to be as lacking in wisdom as he is genuinely clever.

By taking thought the Thalamus cannot be made to feel, nor, on the other hand, can it at all easily be checked if feel it does. Hence those embarrassingly dry eyes at funerals and the welling up of wild emotion on occasions when the intellect had decided on the most rational control. Perhaps it is the intimate connection between the Thalamus and the eyes that gives to visual images their peculiar emotional potency, enabling the most sentimental rubbish on the cinema screen to make our tears flow even while the cerebral mind looks on in high disapproval.

There is another structure within the brain hard to describe and still only slightly understood, yet evidently of immense importance in the development of mental power. This is a network of tissue draped round the stem and Thalamus known as the Diffuse Reticular System. This network, though present already in primitive creatures, contributes to the *learning* which is a basic process in our own mental life. Its function seems to be to forward to most parts of the Cerebrum all information gathered by the senses. The diffuseness of the system, its freedom from specialized automatic functions, suggests that it increases the freedom, the ability to adapt to the changing and unexpected, so necessary for survival on this perilous earth.

Evidently all that is best in a rich creative life comes from the interplay of these two parts of the human brain, one so much more ancient than humanity, the other in its full development as young as our species. It would be false to say that it makes greatness, for although this endowment is in part hereditary, education, social pressures, chance, and above all, perhaps, that incomprehensible thing the personal will, help to determine both the development and the balance of these two instruments of consciousness. Most certainly the will can stimulate the intellect as we have bravely shown to us by all those cripples, dwarfs, and bastards who force it to feats of which it would never have been capable had there been no challenging handicap. The Thalamus of its nature is elusive, but only asks, as did mine, to be allowed the chance of emotional exercise in order to ripen to its full powers.

From the majestic seat of feeling and personality in the Old Brain we rise now to where intellect is enthroned in the New. While the Old Brain in its entirety weighs only some 175 grams in a brain of average size, the twin lobes of the Cerebrum or Cortex weigh as much as 1,200 grams. In the most cerebral of animals, the apes, the New Brain reaches about 350 grams; by such a head do we outstrip our fellow creatures.

The hollow hemispheres of the Cerebrum, joined by a slab of connecting nerve fibres, are composed of an outer covering of grey matter of brain cells accounting for a quarter of the total thickness, and an inner sheet of white matter or nerve fibres. Only those nerve fibres which are healthy and in use have the white coating of myelin which acts as an insulator much like the rubber, silk, and plastic coating of electric flex. In the newborn baby only a few fibres are coated and ready for use, but as the individual grows up, refining the senses and developing the mind, more and more are drawn into active life; the richest and most flexible minds may have the greatest number brought into fullest use. Here, presumably, is the secret of how it is possible to succeed in the specialized education of one faculty.

The grey matter of the Cortex, so familiar in

schools, music-halls and other places of simple jest, is built up of five or six distinct layers of cells, and the identification of cortical grey matter with 'braininess' is better justified than is usual with such simple notions, for upon the number of these layers the complexity of the human intellect in part depends. When a cat looks at a king he can draw upon no more than three cell layers for his conclusions, and this limitation, although undoubtedly it leaves him more content in his untroubled bodily perfection, will prevent him from ever being able to publish a book, or even give a lecture, on the subject of royalty.

The need of the Cerebrum is for as much surface as possible, hence the innumerable wrinkles, folds, and deep fissures that have multiplied and deepened as its swelling hemispheres had to pack into the confining skull. Nearly four-fifths of the surface of the human Cortex is hidden in these creases. I have described the roof of the skull rising like a gently blown bubble during the course of human evolution, but even now the highest brow cannot hold the Cerebrum without this violent folding, and indeed the pressure of the soft grey matter on the inside of the skull is enough to imprint its contours on the bone. That is why when modern men, curious about the history of their own organs of curiosity, take plaster casts of the interior of the skulls of Pithecanthropus and other forebears, they can obtain a rough replica of the swellings, hollows, and raised blood vessels of the brain that experienced and directed a Pleistocene existence.

Although even the trilobites could see dimly and feel their way, swim and scuttle on the sea bed, the forward movement of the seat of consciousness has meant that in man the reception areas for all those faculties linked with consciousness, the nerves serving the senses and the muscular control of limbs and body, have shifted into the Cerebrum. Damage to the Cortex will interfere with these relatively primitive activities as much as with the recently developed human faculties of skilful manipulation, speech, and thought. Such damage has shown that in fact each hemisphere is largely responsible for the opposite side of the body, the nerve fibres from the right-hand side passing over to the left, those from the left to the right. The control centre for the right hand therefore lies in the left hemisphere, and it may be a proof of the original connection between manual skill and the development of articulate speech that in the normal right-handed man or woman the speech centre lies close to that of the hand in the left side of the brain.

All these functions old and new, high and low, are, as I have already suggested, to some extent localized in different regions of the Cortex—a fact which theoretically encourages the antics of phrenologists, even though in practice the degree of development of the various centres cannot possibly show itself in the bumps of the skull. Indeed, the question of localization is as intricate as it is significant, and at present it divides those fearless men who specialize in the eerie pursuit of the living brain into opposing schools. Members of the diagrammatic school, which is, I believe, losing ground, envisage the brain like a county map, allotting every cerebral function a precisely marked and independent region of the Cortex. Their opponents, although they concede that there are specialized centres vital to the maintenance of their function, are inclined to see the whole of the Cerebrum with its ten thousand million cells working as a whole, with huge numbers of non-specialized cells contributing to all our activities. When part of the Cortex is destroyed or removed, provided the damage does not affect the essential centres, the lost function can be relearned; to a remarkable extent new nerve cells can be brought into use to assume the duties of their fallen comrades. This adaptability tells against the extreme diagrammatic school of locationists. Similarly, concentrated education or training can bring more and more nerve cells into active use, so that the acquired specialist skills and understanding of our most various lives can enlarge their contributory regions within the Cortex. Further to complicate the problem, it begins now to appear that the extent to which the second hemisphere reinforces its companion has a decisive influence on brain power. It seems in general that it is not so much the number of cells that is of the greatest significance in making possible high intellectual development, but rather the complexity and ease of communication between them. Perhaps in stupid, unimaginative people well-established lines of communication are used again and again until they become almost automatic. How well one knows the stock response. Lively minds, on the other hand, and the minds of children that are undeveloped but never stereotyped, keep many lines open, drawing messages from many centres, tapping the memories of all their experience. In freaks such as the Calculating Boy one imagines that some few channels must be peculiarly active, perhaps free from blockages or

BUDDHA MEDITATING

". . . learning to control the strange, hidden world of the psyche."

". . . man . . . in modest harmony with nature."

CHINESE SAGE

interruptions normally present. One's own mind boggles at attempting to imagine the convergence of many exceptional attributes, including of course an active Thalamus, required by the brain of genius.

Although every cell in the brain may contribute something to all our more complicated thoughts and actions, the essential centres have their fixed places in the Cortex, and have been reliably mapped in scores of grizzly-looking diagrams displaying the naked brain, smoothly bubbled like a lump of natural meerschaum, with the skull sawn through, or peeled off like the shell of a boiled egg. Men have even made a classificatory system of numbers for its convolutions (as indeed they have for almost everything). It runs up to forty-five numbered parts; my own account will be very much simpler. Smell, taste, and hearing occupy much of the temporal lobe above the ear; sight lies right at the back of the head at about the point where the collar of the average winter coat touches it, but all the nervous impulses set up by vision must be relayed back to it from the Thalamus. Touch is higher up in the back part of the head, while the motor region, controlling muscular movement, forms a band across the top of the head. The intricate pattern of the speech centre spreads along the charmingly named Sylvian Fissure, the deepest, most important fold in the Cortex, which runs obliquely upwards across the temple towards the back of the head. As I have said, in right-handed people speech is controlled from the left hemisphere, in the left-handed from the right.

These are some of the vital points which, if they are damaged, leave the individual permanently defective. But round them and throughout that part of the brain crowded behind the forehead are great areas of Cortex without precise functions. These are the association areas whose spaciousness is peculiar to man, the rich reserves relatively free from specialized tasks which, in ways still wholly mysterious to us, make possible the storage of myriads of memories, numerous as the twittering dead of the underworld, and the working of imagination and intellect. Even the processes of memory, seemingly so much the simplest of the three and coming within the range of things properly explicable by science, cannot as yet be made intelligible. If the temporal lobe is exposed and electrically stimulated, its owner will be beset with vivid memories of days gone by, perhaps scenes from childhood and youth. How this substance, soft like toothpaste, of the nerve cells, and the little threads of nerve fibre running between them, can hold the impressions of a lifetime, and perhaps of previous lifetimes, then project them once more like magic lantern slides showing a girl in a spring orchard, a boy riding with his mother in a carriage, is hard indeed to comprehend. Hard enough to have baffled the most formidable scientific brains of our time, the brains belonging to such great names as Sherrington, Adrian, and Head.

Little as we comprehend their mode of work, we certainly owe to the unspecialized brain cells much of the adaptability which has been so necessary to our evolution and which should do so much for our future history, if we allow ourselves to have one. Together with the Reticular system they make reserves of power and resourcefulness ready to be turned in new directions when mankind needs, or wishes, so to turn.

The fore part of the Cerebrum must appeal to those searching for the attributes of humanity within the skull. The former belief that man was peculiarly distinguished by the growth of this region has now been modified, though not before it left us with the term 'highbrow' to exacerbate our social factions. Other regions have increased in our brains relatively even more than this one. Yet undoubtedly the brain behind the forehead does play a most influential, even if subtly veiled, part in our human attainment. Its role can be readily studied because the stress and distress of modern life have made many wrecks of humanity who prefer the sacrifice of their frontal lobes to the neurotic anxieties which are driving them mad. The surgeon cuts his holes on either side of the forehead (prehistoric man performed a similar operation with flint and without anaesthetic) and slips in his blade to cut the fibres connecting the frontal lobes with the Old Brain, a deed which virtually puts this part of the Cortex out of action. His victim or patient is relieved of his tormenting anxieties and depressions but also of an important part of his humanity. One can say, of course, that he was no good before and is less trouble afterwards, but to my mind suicide would be the choice more worthy of our kind. The results vary with the established character of the subject and occasionally are happy. But the man who has submitted himself to this pruning operation is liable to lose genuine moral responsibility (though not the habit of conformity), higher intellectual grasp and the ability to initiate and carry through any creative idea; he may become tactless, apathetic, and lacking in the emotional energy needed for affection. In many ways, indeed, he might seem to offer the perfect material for a Totalitarian State.

These effects of the voluntary surrender of the frontal lobes are full of interest. First we have to remember that this part of the Cerebrum is intimately connected with the Thalamus, the first centre of the emotions, and through it with the internal and sexual organs. The connection is severed by the surgeon's knife. This in itself, of course, accounts for the lessening of emotional anxieties, for the thalamic energy is taken out of them, but with it goes the mental vitality which is a dear and necessary part of the creative mind. In addition to this loss of energy from the Old Brain there is the sacrifice of the great associative areas of the frontal Cortex itself, a forfeit which must impoverish the highest centres of intellect.

Failures in tact and moral responsibility seem to be due to the loss of certain tracts in the frontal lobes whose strange duty it is to check undesirable activities in other parts of the brain. It seems extraordinary that parts of the brain should have such monitoring duties, but so it is, and when their control is removed the individual cannot, or does not bother, to check rough, insensitive words and behaviour. Monkeys who have been subjected to the operation will even walk or sit on their fellows, evidently oblivious of their outraged feelings. Tactlessness could hardly be carried further.

The weakening in victims of lobotomy of strong personal affection and love is surely most significant. I believe the love of man and woman, resting on perfect sexual union and flowering from these dark roots into the tenderest affection and understanding, to be one of the high achievements of mankind. Indeed, sexual love itself, though I have called it dark because it plunges us into the depths of the unconscious, is in itself a subtle and very human thing. Our love-making can be further removed from the perfunctory copulation of animals than very many other activities of our daily lives, bringing us a marvellous blending of bodily and mental experience, heightened and magnified by a potent emotional charge. It can be experienced like bubbles of pure spirit rising through the dark waters of the unconscious mind.

Christianity has done no worse thing than imposing upon half the world violent and distorted views concerning that fine flower of evolution, the erotic relationship between man and woman. Through condemning it as animal, forbidding the devout to enjoy its delights, the Churches have cut off hosts of poor mortals not only from pleasures of the senses as innocent as the enjoyment of the sun, but also from high spiritual refreshment. They have turned something nobly human into something animal indeed.

In the structure of the fore-brain we can see the instrument for this union of bodily with mental experience. The sexual organs speak directly to the Thalamus, the Thalamus emotionally to the frontal lobes, the seat of some of the most delicate mental powers of man, whence responses can be carried back to the sexual centres. The name Thalamus means 'hidden chamber', and the Greeks themselves often used the word to signify the marriage bed. The name unintentionally chosen by scientists is, then, a happy one, for here we have the marriage bed of body and mind or spirit from which has been born that lovely and much persecuted child, our human love.

I will turn from love to indigestion. One of the very latest discoveries of brain about itself is that the frontal lobes include the cortical motor area for the unconscious processes of the Old Brain in running our internal organs, including the stomach, intestine, and kidneys. Thus when nervous anxieties begin to haunt this part of the brain they have their immediate internal effects, causing ulcers, and high blood pressure through the mismanagement of the kidneys. So it is once more from the regions behind our foreheads that the insecurity and overstrain of our days upset the smooth running of our internal economy, established for us so successfully in the remote and thoughtless past.

I should dearly like to be able to follow this account of the functional anatomy of our brains with a corresponding psychological anatomy. I have just given a mechanical explanation of certain psychosomatic illness, but for the higher realms of mental psychology our brains have as yet put but little effort into self-analysis. Can one identify the various parts of the brain, Old and New, as the seat of collective and personal unconscious, the ego, the Self, and other conceptions of the psychologists? It would be foolish indeed to try any exact mapping, but from the point of view of the historical nature of the brain an exceptional interest attaches to those Jungian conceptions which assume an historical inheritance within the psyche.

While we remain ignorant of the mechanical basis of memory it is difficult to speculate intelligently as to the likely whereabouts of the seat of the collective unconscious which represents, essentially, the generalized experience of the species and its forebears. There seems little doubt that the functions of the personal unconscious are entirely centred in the New Brain, forming a somewhat deeper level, perhaps, of the vast store of ordinary memories stored in the Cortex. Is it possible that the collective unconscious, whose great significance in the creation of cultures is apparent in the next chapter, functions from the Thalamus? Whatever the actual mode of recording memories may be, as the Thalamus, like the outer layers of the Cortex, is composed of grey matter, it seems likely enough that it would be capable of retaining this impression of the ancient experience of our kind which shapes the Jungian archetypes. These archetypes which are built up not by unique experiences, but, it seems, by many common experiences printed upon one another like the repeated exposure of a photographic film, do not give rise to exact images as do individual memories, but to more generalized forms that assume different manifestations in different cultures. Jung himself has called them 'the organs of the pre-rational psyche'. This would seem to be in harmony with impressions received in the Old Brain, while the emotional content of the Thalamus would account for the great strength of the archetypes and their emergence in the religious myths and symbols of all mankind.

I myself, then, would be bold enough to lodge the deepest levels of unconscious mind in the Thalamus, that organ evolved by the amphibians and shared by us with all our fellow creatures who are not more lowly than the frogs. This identification has some significance because, as we have seen, the Thalamus plays an important part in the conscious mind, even while it remains in realms too deep for thought. This would help to make it clearer how the 'unconscious' of the psychologists is able to exercise so profound an effect on consciousness. I suggest that it is in truth not so much unconscious, as an aspect of consciousness altogether distinct from the intellectual centres of the Cerebrum. The ego, plainly, represents some focal point of the powers of this New Brain, while the persona, that stuffed figure which we hold up, a dummy self, in an effort to deceive our fellows, is worked, like a puppet by its wires, by a set pattern of communications in the same organ. Again to me there seems no doubt that the 'integration of the personality' leading to the discovery of the true Self represents the establishment of a right balance between Thalamus and Cerebrum, or perhaps between the whole of the Old Brain and the New; which is also to say between light and darkness, the feminine principle and the masculine.

At this point I find myself forced by an irrepressible inner conviction to put forward an idea far-fetched to the point of incredibility, yet to me convincing. I believe that the mind may project into the outer world not only the images of the psychic content of the brain, but also something of its significant anatomy. All through history and the world men have recognized an abundant mother goddess, whom they assigned to the darkness of the earth and its chthonic realm, and, in extreme contrast, a masculine divinity, a god of light with the Apollonian attributes of intellect, always assigned to a realm in the heavens, often set above the bowl of the sky. Of the two, the mother goddess evidently represents the more primitive image, having already emerged in the Old Stone Age. The dark hidden chamber of the Thalamus, the seat of the feminine aspect of the conscious mind, lies as the supporting platform below the arching hemispheres of the masculine, intellectual Cerebrum very much as the earth lies below the apparent vault of the sky. Is it not possible that we have expressed in these world-wide religious symbols an image of the living forms that the evolution of consciousness has built within our own skulls?

I have now anatomized the brain, given some account of the mental and physical employment of its various parts, and even ventured to identify the activities of certain organs of the brain with some of the basic concepts of Jungian psychology, attempting to apply the mental pattern of the psyche to the evolutionary pattern of the brain. (In all this I have certainly sometimes fallen into the snares of whose existence I had warned myself; my mind is too weak, the language too clumsy for me to be able altogether to avoid them. I am confident only of having escaped the sin of the 'nothing but' approach, that idiotic desire of the smallest and meanest type of scientific mind to make human life appear as small and mean as itself. This is the approach which logically should lead the possessors of such minds to see in St. Paul's Cathedral nothing but a collection of blocks of Portland stone, in their mothers a few pounds of chemicals, and in their own observations some verbal rubbish. I do not think I have anywhere used words to suggest that the achievements of intellect are no more than the mechanical products of the brain cells of the Cerebrum, or that love is to be found in the grey matter of the Thalamus and frontal lobes).

In all this we have come no nearer to understanding how the 'mind is attached to the body'; indeed, as I have said, we have not as yet solved the preliminary and far more amenable problem of how memory, learning by experience, is stored among those ten thousand million cells. In the past few years of our life on earth, however, our brains have begun to pry out some news not of the nature of mind, but of how it works. It has been known among us for some time that just as the beating of the heart involves the discharge of electricity, so in the conscious brain there are rhythmic electrical discharges generated by its own nerve cells. The amount of current involved is tiny—just enough in the whole brain to make a visible glow in a torch bulb—yet we have now learnt how to amplify it so greatly that if a million or so nerve cells fire together, the resulting electrical discharge can be made conspicuously visible. The Cerebral Cortex has used its cunning to design a marvellous machine to map its own activity. This machine, though it is to demonstrate so small and essentially insignificant a part of the brain's activity, requires a whole room to itself. The owner of the brain to be tested lies on a couch with electrodes applied to his skull and these connect with an oval arrangement of cathode tubes forming an electric chart of the top of the Cerebrum. As the minute oscillations of current within the brain assert themselves, the cathode screens light up, so mapping both the position and duration of the impulses. This prosaically named toposcope does in fact almost succeed in suggesting the beautiful account of the working brain written by Sir Charles Sherrington, when he described it as an 'enchanted loom where millions of flashing shuttles weave a dissolving pattern, always a meaningful pattern though never an abiding one'. And again: 'A sparkling field of rhythmic flashing points with trains of travelling sparks hurrying hither and thither.'

Among these dissolving patterns or rhythms, a number are regular enough to be recognized and, to some slight extent, interpreted. A slow one sets in with disease, perhaps indeed as a resistance against it like the feverish rising of body heat, and can be used to detect the presence of tumours; one unusual rhythm goes with epilepsy and yet another is provoked by anger—an electric storm in a brainpan.

All of these electrical patterns vary with the individual man or woman, and can be read as expressions of their nature, even of their character. One in particular appeals to the imagination through such indications of individuality. This is known as the Alpha-rhythm, a rhythm of some ten cycles to the second radiating from the region of the visual centres at the back of the head like the regular flashes of a lighthouse. Yet in purpose it is much better compared to a searchlight scanning the heavens with a regular sweep, then checking when it encounters its object, the aeroplane coming into its range from outer space. Or, to escape the tyranny of the machine image, it can be likened to an angler casting rhythmically until he gets a strike. For the Alpha-rhythm represents the alertness of the waking mind when it is quiescent but, as it were, seeking work to do. Its measured rhythm of ten cycles to the second persists while the individual lies with eyes closed and mind at rest, but is likely to subside when the eyes are opened or the mind forced to concentrate.

It is here that we find the intimations of individuality. In people who habitually think wholly in visual images the Alpha-rhythms are almost absent, in those who always think verbally or in abstract terms they continue untroubled when the eyes are open or the mind engaged on a problem, and can only be interrupted by some enforced fixing of the eyes, as in reading aloud. These are the two rare extremes. In most of us the rhythm is strong and regular in rest, but cuts out as soon as the attention is held. It is not difficult to imagine why individuals belonging to the two extreme types find it almost impossible really to understand one another; the worlds inside their heads are different places and an experience comes to them in totally different guise. One deals with it theoretically, logically, though not necessarily with insight; the other responds to a series of brilliantly convincing pictures.

The Alpha-rhythm marks the tireless search for experience of the waking mind. In sleep it wanes and slower pulses take its place, though dreams may make sudden rapid oscillations, whose brief duration is proof of the dreamer's freedom to live through many hours in ten seconds of measured time.

Sleep may itself be a product of the brain's long history; sleep, that irresistible conqueror of consciousness which should be enough to shake the conceited intellectual ego of the Cerebrum out of its delusion of being sole lord and master of the individual. True it may have a chemical explanation, the need to consume poisons accumulated from the ceaseless waking activities of the brain; or again may be due to the desire of other parts of the body to be released from nervous control. But there is also the possibility that it is a habit conditioned by our ancestors' diurnal life, by their inability to hunt or eat during the hours of darkness. Or it may even be a survival from our yet remoter past, from the enforced lapse from consciousness of the amphibians, when their unheated bodies were subjected to the unaccustomed coldness of terrestrial nights. If this is true, then just as they brought the salt sea ashore in their blood stream for us to inherit, so, too, they brought the nightly swoon of sleep.

The electrical impulses generated in the nerve cells and coursing through the nerve fibres come as close as anything we are ever likely to see to being the physical manifestations of thinking. Yet they are more remote from thought or imagination than the lingering trail of a shooting star is from the lump of meteorite. The mere fact that the Alpha-rhythm ceases when the mind becomes active should warn us against thinking of these electric impulses as the passage of thoughts and images in the sense that radio waves are the passage of transmitted sounds. Nor are we in any way at their mercy. When the experimental subject is made angry and the dissolving patterns of his anger flicker across the cathode tubes, he may be able to control his feelings, when immediately the electric impulses are seen to check, waver a little as anger tries to reassert itself, then die away altogether. Will power, the will we saw coming into being so long ago, has won the day and the man kept his temper.

Thus in truth we have not gone far in our pursuit

of the central mystery of our being, what it is that instigates thought, projects images, enjoys sensations, and controls behaviour, the being who is Mozart, Newton, or John Smith. Certainly we no longer believe that mind is a distinct element taking up its residence in the body at some particular point such as the Pineal Eye selected by the dualist Descartes; yet even such a supposed empiricist as a nerve surgeon has written: 'When a patient is asked about the movement which he carries out as a result of cortical stimulation, he never is in any doubt about it. He knows he did not will the action. . . . He knows there is a difference between automatic action and voluntary action. He would agree that something else finds its dwelling place between the sensory complex and the motor mechanism, that there is a switchboard operator as well as a switchboard.' We have seen consciousness coming into existence on earth, evidently a part of the process of life itself, something which is probably inherent in the whole cosmos but here on earth has its strongest concentration in the brain of man; something which strengthens with time, being now already far more powerful than it was a million years ago, and which, if we serve it as we should, may attain far greater force in future civilizations. Viewing the heightening of consciousness in this way we see it as a vast cosmic process; yet we know it is the individual possessor of mind who has counted in that process, who has created the accumulated treasures of history, whether he is a genius making some colossal addition to our cultural wealth—or an ordinary man or woman, thinking, making, as well as they can, rearing children, helping life and consciousness to continue on earth. Surely there is great wonder and mystery here. Its wonder can be denied only by the more trivial kind of scientific materialists, who revel meanly in the belittlements of the 'nothing but' view of life, or by the more trivial kind of philosophers, the logical positivists, who sit on so vast a pile of the debunked follies and illusions of mankind that their heads are in icy clouds and can bring forth nothing.

We shall do best to state the processes of history as they appear to us, and in all humility to marvel at them. Here inside the skull of every one of us is the stuff built up by generation after generation of worms, fish, amphibians, reptiles, mammals, apes, and men, and which generation after generation of men have used to transform the surface of the mother planet. For a long time now there has been no further improvement in the mechanism of the brain, only it has been more fully and subtly used and its products have accumulated, offering each generation a richer birthright than the last. We of the twentieth century have an enormous inheritance, augmented beyond measure by the curiosity which has sent mind back on its own tracks and has now rescued for us memories of the whole vast span of our days. From the cave paintings and carvings of the Stone Age hunters through the creations of Mesopotamia, Egypt, Crete, China, Greece, Rome, Mexico and Peru, Renaissance Europe, and many, many others, we have inherited or rediscovered the works of the rare mind of genius, and also countless pretty things from the hands of craftsmen and the minds of simple people. Each after its fashion, the transcendental and the every-day, helps to bind us together, and makes it easier to see the whole of our history as one.

As, in the much greater stretches of time before humanity itself had come into being, part was added to part of the brain to produce an instrument summarizing the achievements of the whole of time past, so, too, the culture we inherit represents a summary of human history. Thus we can see how every poem, every picture, and other high product of mind holds in itself something of the whole tale of man on earth.

It is impossible to deny the mind's share in the evils of our history, especially the cruelties which have sprung both from its conscious and its unconscious workings. Yet it remains true that the more the whole mind with its powers of thought and imagination has been fully used, the finer, the more deeply human, has the resulting culture been. Mind used at full stretch erects the noble temple, the aspiring church, the comely house; something almost mindless, closer to the animal life of rookery and warren, allows the slum to pile up, the suburb to sprawl out, earth to be riddled and plundered and to fall into squalid decay. History tells us plainly what we should do. Brain, as the instrument of intelligence, has been the prime aim (for those who believe in chance, the main result) of a thousand million years of evolution. It is our duty to use and develop it with all our bodily force, guarding a fine balance between Thalamus and Cerebrum, energy and restraint, imagination and intellect, and to apply it, lovingly, to an ever greater part of our daily lives and their earthly matrix.

In days of peace, it has been said, there is no common goal for man, nothing to encourage his endeavour. Who, looking at our slums, our industrial squalor, at our ignorance and the poverty of our inner life, can yet believe this? We can all do something to use and refine, to refine by use, the exquisite instrument housed for us within the curved bones of the skull.

But I have advanced into the present too soon. In the last chapter I had only reached the point where, after those first brilliant flashes which so unexpectedly illumined the dark caves of the hunters, mind was about to create its own world, a civilized human setting from which it could shine forth in full radiance.

civilization 6

The building of human worlds

The human body has been shaped and completed and the marvellous instrument housed within the skull has tuned itself to the production of language and art. Now man is about to move forward to the creation of great cultures and wide civilizations. Consciousness has already destroyed his unity with his natural surroundings, with the living creatures once his companions of the evolutionary way, and beyond them with the inorganic world in which man and beast alike were rooted. As history advances he will use his reason to isolate himself more and more from this natural matrix, will turn against and exploit it, regarding the whole stuff of earth as material for his will. Man will close his body within house and city, and his experience within the walls of his intellectual constructions. Only in the deeper levels of his being a power will remain prompting him always to seek to regain his lost communion with the universe, inspiring him to seek God behind a thousand different masks.

Before advancing him to the seeming security of civilization it will be well to reflect on the inheritance which, willy nilly, he carried with him from the past. The four walls of human existence are not so substantial or exclusive as we like to think at all times except when our confidence is shaken by the earthquakes of private or public crisis. Man may lock the doors and bar the gates, but his own body and mind have come to him from the wilderness outside and bring something of the wilderness with them. There are few physical parts he does not possess in common with the animals; the very frog in the ditch shares much of his bodily equipment. We have probed to the ancient foundations of the brain. With flesh and bone, moreover, he inherits passions, emotions, and imaginative forms, never to be wholly subdued or left behind.

A man can be so sure of being John Smith, of tomorrow being Monday and the earth there to give him what is his by right, that he forgets these snug walls of his are held only by the power of the human mind. The wilderness is within and without. If mind weakens and lets go there will be no Sunday and Monday, no content or form; all divisions will fall and familiar streets lead nowhere. What is more, this mental power is not the secure private possession of the individual, but is handed on in trust to him by his parents and his whole society. Infants reared by wolves have grown into near-wolves, hunting on all fours, howling and baying; years of patient training failed fully to humanize them. Revolutionaries, iconoclasts, and the eternally idealistic young of the species do not understand this perilous fragility of civilization and scorn with ungrateful arrogance the painful, laborious additions made to it by hundreds of generations of their ancestors, the ordinary and the gifted together. They see the failings and injustices of human affairs and instead of marvelling that they are not worse among poor creatures striving to live and to create in the bewilderment of their consciousness, believe that if they overthrew all that has been achieved they could build it up again free from blemish. I wish I could find words to convey the mad folly of this attitude, words which would be sharp enough to cut windows in the four walls of man's refuge and enable him to see himself as he is, a creature raised from slime, clinging in utter ignorance of his fate to the surface of a planet. Certainly new ideas should compete with stale ones just as the young must always compete with the old, but there has never before, I think, been such a lack of natural piety towards history or such deliberate plans for wrecking its achievements as are found in some men today. In this plight of ours, to shout of human rights, to destroy what has been created through thousands of years is the madness of the padded cell.

We have no rights on earth save those flimsy ones that each society must struggle to maintain for itself. We have no absolute rights, but only the duty to enrich experience and heighten consciousness.

It is good, I think, to have chosen this moment when we are on the threshold of civilization to consider both the power of the dark and the primitive which we must bring to it in our ancient persons, and also the fragility of the hard-won inheritance it enshrines. Civilization is like a skin of ice above bottomless waters.

Yet the darkness below, through infinitely dangerous, is also full of treasure. Examination of the brain has helped to show why it is that to live by the intellect and reason of civilization alone would be as cold as the ice of my simile. The body and the unconscious mind are the source of most of our joys and highest creations. I shall return to this again and again for it is one of my themes. At this moment I want only to think of one form of these treasures of the deep which is of special significance for the growth of cultures.

We have looked inside the skull casket at the human brain, we know how much of it has been built up in animality, how much is of recent and peculiarly human growth. Just as the substance and structure of the brain come to us from the past, so, some of us believe, do many valuable mental furnishings. Animals are born with instincts acquired through millions of years of historical experience; the weaver bird can braid his nest, the singing bird sing, untaught; the tiny new-born kangaroo crawls through the dense forest of the maternal fur to reach the unknown pouch and its teats; the piglet staggers straight from the vagina's mouth to fight for sucking space on the maternal mountain-side. In us these physical instincts are fewer and less strong; instead our progress through time seems to have left us with memory-shapes buried deep in the unconscious mind. When great psychical experiences open a way for them into consciousness, they rise to inspire the symbolism of religion and art. It is when the symbols of ritual, of poetry, painting, or music chime with these memory-shapes, echoing within the mind in perfect harmony, that we experience the magical delight of holiness and art. Of all artists perhaps William Blake possessed the deepest, most direct insight and so was best able to create images to strike such magic chimes.

What is the final significance of the intuitions which come to us from these memories? Pavlov has shown how a dog's mouth will water at the mere sound of a bell when its ringing has long been associated with the pleasures of food. Is our response to the magic symbols no more than an historically conditioned association of the mind? Some would say yes. But I am among those who hope (no more than hope) that the primordial images which have been accumulating since we were one with the fabric of nature bring us intimations of cosmic meaning. Intellectual force is needed to raise them and express them in symbolic forms, but it may well be that they whisper to us of cosmic secrets beyond the grasp of intellect.

Thus some twelve thousand years ago we have man standing ready as the earthly bearer of full consciousness, ready to stride forward towards his strange future, yet also bearing in his body and unconscious mind the inheritance from his enormous past. As the ice began to melt around him, the face of our planet was greatly changed. The sea-level rose, and while forests spread over many of the open hunting grounds of Asia, Europe, and North America, other regions formerly well watered became desert.

In Europe, where the human spirit had risen to its first great achievement, the Stone Age hunters no longer enjoyed the abundant food supplies that had made possible the development of their superb art. Instead of the vast herds of game animals of the steppe and tundra, they now had to hunt the smaller, more scattered game of the forests and heaths, or learn to hook, net, and spear fish, and gather limpets, mussels, and other poor stuff which formerly they might have scorned. It was a rough challenge, but man had gone too far now not to accept it. His psychic energy was flowing out into the world, and he would not again, as he had before, retreat passively in the face of changing conditions.

There was, however, a pause before the revolutionary response was accomplished, a pause of five thousand years which can be regarded as a winter time intervening between the last great age of the hunters in Europe and the first triumph of the farmers in Asia. The seed must have been in the ground; perhaps there were men and women making tentative essays in husbandry, but as yet there was nothing to suggest the abundance of the new life that was germinating. This Middle Stone Age appears now as one of recoil and quiescence.

The exact region in the Old World where our ancestors began to grow cereal crops and domesticate animals has not yet been precisely recalled. It was somewhere in South-west Asia between Palestine and Iran, where several species ancestral to early domesticated breeds both of plants and of animals occur in the wild state.

There can be no greater instance in all our history of momentous events being determined blindly and without intention. Somewhere a few men had the idea of taking control of herds of wild cattle and flocks of sheep instead of going after them as hunters. Probably there were droughts and men provided food and water for the desperate animals, gradually making them dependent, and then wholly tamed and enslaved. Within a thousand years these first shepherds and cattlemen had discovered how to breed new domestic strains better suited to their human needs.

Somewhere not far distant and at very much the same time, a few individuals, and it is likely they were women in all their patience, had the idea of sowing seed grains in good soil and waiting for them to grow and ripen. Soon they, too, had changed the wild forms by selective seeding till they had plots of wheat and barley giving much larger yields than any natural crop. Outside a cave on Mount Carmel only a few yards from the terrace where we found the apish skeleton, I have myself helped to uncover the remains of men and women who contributed to this great historical event. We picked out of the powdery soil the black, glossy obsidian flakes which they had fitted into carved antler hafts to make sickles, and saw how on some the edge was polished from cutting dry stalks. We cleared out small pits in the rock where they had pounded grain into rough flour. Yet these people still lived mainly on gazelles and other wild game, and they carved images of them even on their sickle hafts, much as the Stone Age hunters had carved ibex and reindeer on their spear-throwers. We cannot be sure that these cave dwellers sowed what they reaped, for they may have used their sickles on harvests growing wild on the fertile coastal plain. Yet undoubtedly these individuals whose huddled skeletons I have seen with shell headbands still clinging to their skulls and necklaces tumbling below their grinning jaws, played some pioneer part in that practice of agriculture which has gone on ever since through seven thousand cycles of the year.

Not only was the gradual invention of husbandry one of the most important historical events, the necessary preparation for the flowering of civilized life, it was also of great psychological significance. With it will was strengthened on earth and man cut out more sharply from his natural matrix. For hundreds of thousands of years men had been imposing imagined forms on dead matter such as stone, bone, and wood, but now they dared to direct and shape living creatures for their own purpose. The brain was taking control over more bodies than its own.

The Old Stone Age hunters had been aware of a difference between themselves and wild animals, but they were very close to them and experienced the excitement and awe expressed in their art. Animals and men alike were free citizens of the kingdom of nature, going out to eat, to kill or be killed. But as the beasts were subjected, man saw them as an inferior creation existing only to serve his needs. In assuming absolute control over many of his fellow creatures he helped to convince himself that he alone was shaped in the image of God. A few millennia after they had abandoned the wild, wandering life of hunters on a primeval globe, the peoples of Southwest Asia were beginning to express this new idea of their relationship with nature in the form of creation myths, including the version which has come down to us through the book of Genesis from Babylonia.

In domesticating animals and plants men also domesticated themselves. Even pastoralism meant the sacrifice of complete freedom of movement and the acceptance of routine duties, while in those regions where agriculture was a serious concern, members of our species were for the first time tied fast to the land. We have recently learned much of the loss of freedom that goes with a gain in security; here was the beginning of it. Docile flocks and herds, full granaries, pushed back the fear of starvation and of sudden death by claw, tusk, or fang, and made it possible to rear larger families. But the liberty, the excitement and, above all, the unexpectedness of the hunting life had gone; communities were fixed in one place or within a small range and every man, woman, and child had to undertake those chores that must be repeated day after day as far as the mind can see.

The human male has never forgotten the hunting life which was the habit of mankind for a period a hundred times longer than his history as a farmer and citizen. Even now to be able to hunt, shoot, and fish is the highest privilege of social standing or financial success. Good, fresh meat and furs, too, are among the privileges of the rich. It is one of the ironies of history that having achieved all he has, man now struggles to enjoy so many of the things which his unregenerate ancestors took for granted ten thousand years ago.

Perhaps it was to compensate themselves for the monotony of the peasant life that our ancestors were early willing to take so much trouble to intoxicate themselves. Men began to cultivate the vine, the finest of all sources of alcoholic enthusiasm, almost or quite as soon as they cultivated grain.

The hunters may have brewed liquors; there have been few peoples at any time or in any part of the world who have not found some means of intoxicating themselves. But living before either will or intellect had been developed and hardened by use, the Old Stone Age tribesmen probably had a low threshold dividing the conscious from the unconscious mind, and so could attain ecstatic excitement and trance with the help only of drums, dancing, and the like. However this may have been, since the time he became a cultivator man has been ready to lavish time, labour, patience, ingenuity, and sensibility on this business of making himself more or less drunk, showing a divine discontent in his determination to alter the state of consciousness to which evolution has brought him. He at once longs to change it, just as he changes his face with paint and strange ornaments. From the Rhine to the Mediterranean, from the Caucasus to Palestine untold lifetimes of work, untold acres of soil have been willingly devoted to the vine. Now the patchwork of vineyards has spread throughout the world. In the Orient when whole populations are near starvation rice is still fermented and distilled, and in the Americas the spiky plants of the mezcal cactus stand in vast vegetable armies, their straight lines rising and falling over hills where soil is precious, waiting for the Indians to cut out their hearts and collect the gathering liquid for pulque and tequila.

Grapes, mezcal, potatoes, barley, rice, sugar, apples, plums, juniper—it seems half the vegetable kingdom has been forced to pay tribute in alcohol. Or, when not wholly wedded to alcohol, men have resorted instead to the coffee bean, the tea and tobacco leaf, the betel nut, to poppy seed and yet more potent herbs, until, smoking, chewing, drinking, they could see the world transformed about them. So human beings have devoted enormous energies and resources to changing their apprehension of the world, and have been equally willing to endure any resulting miseries. How many million hangovers have been suffered since the New Stone Age? All this has been done and endured willingly, yet very often against the solemnly stated intentions of the intellect and its morality. There have been men who have beaten the drum in temperance parades while disappearing on blinds once a month. Has it ever been that by taking thought man could finally master the unconscious mind?

For just like the desire to fight, intoxication is in part atavistic, expressive of a longing to throw off the painfully forged bonds of intellect and self-consciousness and enjoy excitement, abandon, detachment from the self and a world not too logically ordered. Many peoples have accepted it as a holy state, others as one necessary to the balance of the light and dark in man. Even Socrates, intellectual pioneer though he was, accepted this view and himself took part in religious orgies. Probably it would be good for most modern men to be thoroughly drunk once or twice a year, but Saturday nights and Bank Holidays are a poor exchange for the riotous license of the old seasonal festivals.

Recently Aldous Huxley wrote that we should accept our bent for intoxication as the pagans did, but change from alcohol to some cunningly blended drug. I agree with his general idea, for it is a tribute to the need to nourish the darkness in us, but I doubt whether solitary drug-taking can compensate for the social abandonment sought by the followers of Bacchus.

I put it forward as at least a partial truth, that the early invention of wine and barley beer went with man's first relinquishment of the freedom of the hunting life and his acceptance of the settled peasant habit necessary to the birth of civilization.

Until now men had always lived at large, shiftingly. The cave, it is true, had made a fixed point to which a family group might return season after season, perhaps even for generations. It is true, too, that the hunters, fishers, and fowlers of the Middle Stone Age had their flimsy huts scattered among the forests, by riversides or on heaths, their fishing posts, and strand-looping settlements on the foreshore where they lived long enough to accumulate vast rubbish leaps of shell and bone. Yet in many ways these dwellings were close to those of animals: places where nature offered shelter or food.

The new farms and villages were very different. They were centres of small man-made domains, surrounded by fields, outbuildings, irrigation systems, wells, granaries, and store pits, centres of possession and of the products of labour accumulated through centuries. Men or women could hope to rear children in the homes where they themselves had been born. Man had settled down, and on his familiar surroundings he came to bestow the affection that one feels for things made by one's hands, places associated with childhood memories, with adventures, friends and sweethearts living or dead. They were further hallowed by the spirits of all those ancestors whose powers death had strengthened even while it made them invisible.

In these earliest villages, too, neighbourliness must have been born with its loyalty and kindness, its envy, inquisitiveness, and censoriousness. The hunters had lived together in one enclosed space where all experience was shared in common, but now each hut or house was its own world where things could be made, said, done in something like privacy, where there could be secrets and food for gossip.

In their houses the women could establish themselves in peace, though most certainly not in comfort; they did not have to expect at any moment to set out on long treks or hunting trips when all possessions would have either to be abandoned or carried on their backs; with doors and fences they were to some slight extent liberated from the perpetual burden and nuisance of young children. As a result they devised new crafts, all of them representing products that have remained a necessary part of our everyday existence. They learnt that clay, if it was cleaned, kneaded, and fired, became hard and impervious, giving them vessels serviceable for the mixing, cooking, and storing of the dairy produce, the porridge and other cereal messes that were a part of the new way of life. Thus these women potters were not only the first of mankind deliberately to take some of the substance of the earth and change its chemical constitution for a creative purpose, but at the same time made it possible to advance the art of cooking, hitherto limited to roasting on spits or hot stones. They also, though how innocently, began the provision of the surest of all the forms of evidence enabling us, their successors, to rescue something of their history from oblivion. The peoples themselves are vanished, and all their achievements merged into the general stream of culture; often their villages lie hidden under desert wastes, but the fragments of clay, once so yielding to the shaping brain and hand, survive for us to find and interpret. We have learnt that certain shapes, textures, colours, and designs could only be made by particular peoples at particular times, and so even their broken sherds enable us to follow their makers along the trails of prehistory.

The second great attainment of women working in the ancient farming communities was the weaving of cloth. Probably the simple interlacing of twigs and rushes for baskets and matting preceded it, but cloth making demanded two further inventions of an ingenious and not very obvious kind—the weaving loom and also a method for spinning short lengths of fibre or wool into a long and stable thread. At first no doubt the woman span by rolling the threads with her hand on her bare thigh, but before long she developed the pendant spindle, and from that time until today always in some part of the world there have been women busy teasing the soft wool from the distaff and twisting it with skilled fingers while the weighted spindle whirls like a top as it hangs at their sides. I have myself watched an old woman spinning in this fashion no further from Lancashire and Lyons than the island of Majorca.

If there was ever a time when women knew equality with men, or even were in the ascendancy, it was when our forebears were first becoming settled cultivators. They had left the natural world where bodily strength counted for so much, but the human world into which they were moving had not yet become much elaborated. In this world of primitive farming woman was mistress of many important crafts, and, until the introduction of the plough, was everywhere the cultivator of the fields. The small, self-contained community suited her nature and abilities, while her role as the bearer of children must have been highly honoured at a time when children were needed and the spirit of fecundity was alive in society.

The religious cults of this New Stone Age reflect the power of the feminine principle. I do not doubt that then as now, prompted by some image hidden in the unconscious, men identified woman with the earth and its fertility. Thus while the Great Goddess had already come to birth in the minds of hunters wishful for an abundance of wild game, she must now have gained greatly in power as the raising of crops and the breeding of domestic animals occupied men's minds and days. It was she, surely, who was invoked when the lifeless grain had to be buried in the soil in the hope of its resurrection; she who multiplied the lambs and calves. So her image and her worship became widespread. In the religious myths of the Egyptians, Sumerians, and other ancient peoples as they emerge into history we can recognise the Goddess standing behind all later-comers to their pantheons. She was Hathor the Egyptian cow-goddess; she was the Sumerian Ishtar. Agricultural peoples assigned to her as lover and as son the young god who in his many guises dies in order to be born again, as the grain had to be buried in the darkness of the earth before it could sprout into new life.

It was not only in the cradle lands of agriculture in the Middle East that the feminine principle was honoured and the Great Goddess enthroned. Their rule was characteristic of the pioneer stages of husbandry, and is found among all those peoples who spread the practice of farming round the Mediterranean and through Europe during the third and second millennia Before Christ. Indeed, in the great rock-cut and earth-fast tombs of these pioneers we see the chthonic aspect proper to the cult of the feminine principle manifested with full force. By the shores of the western Mediterranean and in the west of Europe we find images of the Goddess cut on the walls of tombs, breasts carved on stones at the portal and phallic pillars within the burial chambers, all serving to remind us that these tombs, the centre of the ritual life of their communities, did not represent a morbid cult of the dead but rather the idea of fertility, of death leading to rebirth.

The cult of the Great Goddess reached its most heightened intensity, however, in Malta, seemingly a holy island where the ways of the New Stone Age were deliberately prolonged in a fervent religious conservatism, and where, perhaps, the dead were ferried for consignment into the sacred soil, the body of the divinity. Here modern man has returned to uncover vast temples built of massive stone blocks or cut into the native rock. In the temples were found images of the Goddess or her followers, some seated, others stretched on couches, all magnificent in their opulent flesh—the breasts full as melons, the enormous thighs and belly expressive of divine abundance.

One of the oddest spectacles I have ever seen was in the prehistoric gallery of the British Museum after it had been burnt by incendiary bombs. Ash had showered into a case of these Maltese statuettes, sliding softly down the huge limbs until they were partially veiled in it. With their voluptuous curves showing through the dust of destruction, the figures sat in monumental calm, proclaiming woman's faith, half-stupid and half-wise, that come what may life must be born, and born again.

These early farming societies with their feminine values were weakened by the rise of cities, trade and empires, and more widely, as in Bronze Age Europe, by repeated conquests at the hands of nomadic pastoral peoples, always much given to warfare, authority, and the stern Father God of the masculine principle. This change, accomplished throughout much of the Old World between the expansion of cities in the third millennium and the defeat of the old tomb-building peoples of Europe during the second, can, if we wish, be identified with the event that Engels described as 'the great historical defeat of the female sex'. It is true that women were probably never again so powerful as they were before these historical events, yet in another sense the defeat of the feminine principle is not one that can be fixed in time; it has suffered and will continue to suffer many defeats—the industrial revolution caused a major one—but it must always rise again for it corresponds to convictions, needs, and desires deep-seated in us all.

Today many people long to see it strengthened in the life of Western man.

If man was beginning to establish his control of wild plants and animals about seven thousand years ago, by the end of the fourth millennium farms and villages had spread over much of the fertile land of the Middle East; in Persia, Mesopotamia, Syria, Palestine, and Egypt the landscape had become, for the first time in the world, in large part the creation of human labour. For thousands upon thousands of years our kind had made no more mark on the planet than a few burnt patches and tracks through forest or across open wastes, and an occasional hut. Now in this one small region of the earth's surface, surrounded still by four-fifths of a globe of undisturbed nature, there were clusters of houses, spreading fields and roadways, tens of thousands of animals living under man's control. There were still no wheeled vehicles on the roads, no boats on the rivers and seas, no mills or water-wheels; nearly everything had to be done by the direct energy of the human body. Yet it is astonishing if one looks at the everyday existence of this time, without attaching the undue importance to technology which is one of our main errors, how much already it had in common with our own. Most of the products advertised today in our underground tunnels had their counterpart in these New Stone Age communities. Clothes of woven wool and linen; such ornaments as were fashionable; houses with roofs as good as those of the Abbey Building Society, and neatly plastered rooms; wine, ales, with beef, mutton, cheese, and wheat bread as the main foods served from decorated crockery; probably already some range of cosmetics—beautiful ornamented palettes designed for grinding malachite and other alluring tints for the olive-skinned beauties of the Nile valley were, one remembers, among the finest products of the pre-dynastic Egyptians. It is astonishing with what speed the peoples of the Middle East advanced from an existence utterly unlike that of civilized man, a life still deeply rooted in animal habit, to conditions nearly comparable with our own. When we think of the Old Stone Age's million years of hardly perceptible change, of the hundred thousand years or less of the progressive late Old Stone Age, the long pause of the Middle Stone Age, and then these mere three or four thousand years of revolutionary development in the New Stone Age, we are overcome by a sense of the acceleration in human history which has now attained so terrifying an impetus. For now a decade brings changes demanding much greater adaptations in our habits of body and mind than a millennium did, even among the pioneer farmers. Standing back to watch this gathering speed of change which hurls our species along faster and faster like a body falling through space, it is hard indeed not to be convinced that some total crisis, and a crisis in some way preordained, is already close at hand.

In the arc of land curving from the Nile valley through Palestine and Syria to the Iranian highlands where the earth's surface was first cultivated by man, the earliest villages had sprung up mainly among the hills. Palestine is the site of the first large walled settlement as yet recalled by modern man, the considerable town whose little cemented houses are being found below the accumulated layers of ancient Jericho. Yet the first high civilizations flowering in rich cities grew up on the floors of the great river valleys of the Nile, the Tigris, and the Euphrates. This primacy of the valleys was in part due to a further shift to the northward of the rain belts which, well after the end of the Ice Age, had still watered even so far south as the Sahara. In the valleys the new desiccation could be outfaced, for river waters and irrigation took the place of rain. Partly it was because once the peasants had succeeded in the immense task of winning farmlands from the swamps and thickets of the valley bottom, annual floods spread a fresh deposit of fertile soil over the fields, enabling heavy crops to be raised year after year on the same ground. The fortunate inhabitants of these valleys could settle down, multiply, and still have great resources left to nourish the craftsmen and labourers needed to create the possible graces of city life.

So between five and six thousand years ago, again acting with the total lack of intention characteristic of all the great events in its history, mankind began to adopt a mode of life which has its nearest counterparts among creatures remote from us biologically—the ants, bees, and wasps. At the centre of the insect community and holding it together is the physical power of the queen; at the centre of these new human communities, inspiring them and holding them together was an imaginative force, the idea of presiding divinity. In both Egypt and Mesopotamia the temples stood at the heart of the city, in the Asian valleys often raised high above all other buildings on the summit of a ziggurat, an artificial mountain of a kind familiar to us still under the name of the Tower of Babel. The citizens of Memphis, too, lived always in sight of the tombs of their god-kings, those early Pharaohs whose pyramids were among the first, and for thousands of years the greatest, proofs of the colossal energy which can be commanded by human imagination implemented by human will. For Kufru's pyramid these mental forces, working in minds only a few generations from primitive peasants, caused nearly two and a half million blocks, each one weighing from two or three tons, to be quarried, transported, and erected in a perfect and entirely original geometric form.

Just as the temples and other religiously inspired buildings dominated their cities architecturally, so too they dominated both the spiritual and everyday life of the people and formed the magnetic centre of their being. The idea spread by narrow rationalists who hate the unconscious springs of imagination that the priests and divine rulers contrived to impose a tyranny upon unwilling citizens and peasants, is as false as it is silly and destructive. These earliest cities grew as spontaneously, as organically as plants, and no organic body can grudge the nourishment it gives to its own highest products whether they are flowers or temples.

The gods and all that surrounded them were the supreme creation of man's unconscious mind and his creative imagination, yet fittingly enough it was they who stimulated the first exercise of his purely intellectual powers. The temple priests were challenged to find means for measuring and recording time, space, and quantity. Empirically, struggling from day to day with problems now so familiar but then altogether strange, they met the challenge. The temple magazines were piled high with goods; in Sumeria for example they might hold barley and wheat, sesame seed, vegetables, dried fruits and fish, beer and wine, wool and hides, and raw materials such as stone, wood, and rushes for increasing and embellishing the buildings. All this vast store needed to be counted, divided up, issued in various amounts to different people. Then the temple owned fields, orchards, date groves and vineyards of all shapes and sizes. Their area and likely yield had to be computed. The whole welfare of the community depended upon the proper observance of the ritual year with the celebrations that followed the cycle of the seasons, while the gods might make themselves known in the movements of the heavenly bodies. So the gods' priestly servants were forced into mathematics and geometry, into astronomy and the making of calendars, and also, the most testing of all their challenges, were obliged to devise means for setting all these things down so that they might be communicated to others.

If the Stone Age cave painters showed astonishing imaginative originality, these Egyptian and Sumerian priests showed an equally marvellous originality in intellectual penetration. They were born into a vague, fluid world where no one had ever thought of measuring the teeming, divine abundance of life. They took the bodily parts evolution had given them, used the breadth of a finger, the span of a hand, the length of a foot for units of measurement; they calculated the movements of the sun and moon and divided time, which had been slipping past unmeasured since the world began, into hours, months, and years. They were born into a world where nothing had ever been recorded except in the cells of the brain, and they devised signs and pictures which could be cut or painted on durable materials, securing numbers, names, and events which until then had drifted away into oblivion.

The invention of writing, which began during the fourth millennium B.C., is a doubly momentous event in this chronicle of man. At the time it helped to heighten and clarify consciousness and perpetuate its discoveries, enriching the growth of cultures almost as much as the original shaping of speech. And for us, looking back, it opens a way into men's minds after the long ages when we have had to judge them only from the work of their hands. One can learn something from everyday things, more from works of art, but when at last words are inscribed on stone, clay, and wood, then our ancient forebears can speak to us directly, telling us in poetry, myths, and histories their experience of life during the dawn of civilization.

Learning to write was one of the significant steps taken by our kind to bring the world into full consciousness and mental life. The process had begun when the eyes of such elementary creatures as the trilobites recorded images of light and shade; it was well advanced when the pioneers of life on land developed the senses of smell, taste, and hearing, and perfected those of sight and touch. Man and man alone carried it much further, first creating language, imposing the word upon the flux of nature and enabling mind to convey experience of it to mind, and now with infinite ingenuity devising signs by which the silent, invisible thoughts and impressions streaming through his brain, and his spoken words fleeting away on the air, could be pinned down and communicated to other minds throughout all time and round all the horizons of the earth.

The Egyptians and Sumerians were the joint founding fathers of our civilization. Because they built in stone, the triumphs of the Egyptians were never forgotten, and it was long believed that they had led the way alone. As soon, however, as our curiosity had discovered the mounds formed by the accumulated ruin and rubbish of the cities of the Two Rivers and had cut down to their ancient foundations, we knew that Asia, too, had been in the van. Perhaps the Sumerians were cleverer, leading the way in mathematics and in the invention of writing and in devising new methods and skills, but the Egyptians show a higher genius in art, more subtle moral and religious thought, and a more graceful urbanity in their habits and possessions. Certainly there was some contact between them. Traders went from Asia into Africa carrying goods in their packs, ideas in their heads, and both were seized upon by their customers. Novelty has always been the one commodity our species could not resist whatever the cost. Thus the two peoples stimulated one another, though it seems each would have achieved the step from village to city alone.

Evidently, then, for an understanding of the history of consciousness it is of profound interest to look more deeply into these valleys and discover how far the cultures that blossomed from the minds of the two races of man differed, how far they display a common human inheritance.

In modern Egypt the contrast between the desert and the sown is absolute. The sinuous green strip of the irrigated lands flanking the Nile runs between grey and yellow wastes of rock and sand. Yet in pre-dynastic and well into historical times the contrast was much less; the wadis running down into the valley were full of vegetation and wild life, and Pharaohs and nobles could mount up through the cliffs separating valley from desert to hunt lion, antelope, and many other creatures that have now withdrawn far to the south. Nevertheless the hundreds of miles of the river's course closed between the parallel lines of cliff, made a kind of forcing frame within which we can watch man growing from savagery to civilization, from the hunting life of the Old Stone Age through the lowly peasant life of the pre-dynastic New Stone Age to the climax of the Old Kingdom, when, sudden as the rising of a rocket, Egyptian culture soared up to a height of achievement from which many of the arts could afterwards only decline.

Here, as always in history, the character of the land can be seen shaping and colouring the character and outlook of its people. The Nile valley was secure, enclosed and cut off from the rest of the world; there could be no setting more likely to encourage a united nation full of conservatism and individuality. Once the earlicst Pharaohs had succeeded in uniting the old tribal areas into the Kingdom of the Two Lands of Upper and Lower Egypt, the people of the whole valley remained a single peaceful nation able to maintain its deliberately conservative culture for some three thousand years. The exact symmetry of the valley, with the sun swinging daily across its naked skies, gave a symmetry to the Egyptian's thought, making him love to maintain harmony by the balancing of opposites—as was gracefully symbolized in the

Double Crown in which the slender white cone for Upper Egypt balanced the golden snake chaplet of Lower Egypt.

The same familiarity with the two lines of cliff seen every day against the sky seems to have inspired Egyptian artists with a natural fondness for cubical constructions, in sharp contrast with the conical forms beloved of the Sumerians, a people whose deepest feelings were turned towards the hills.

With the symmetry of landscape went the absolute cyclical regularity of the annual flood upon which the life of the whole nation turned. Living in so well-defined and orderly a world it is only fitting that the Egyptians should have set up for their ideal of living a perfect and unchanging order in which man and nature and the gods conformed and were at one. Pharaoh stood at the crux of the whole system. He was no mere regent of the gods, this ruler of Egypt, but himself divine. Each Pharaoh was the god Horus, the son of Isis and Osiris and the son whom Osiris himself became when resurrected after his dismemberment. Thus with the gods immanent in the sun, the soil, the river of Egypt, Pharaoh represented the perpetual life and prosperity of the people, divinely renewed every year by the Nile's fertilizing flood. This cosmic harmony the Egyptians knew as *ma'at*, a conception which included the maintenance of justice and a moral order. Every individual citizen could contribute to it by living a seemly life of conformity within his society.

Within this cosmic pattern, within a contract embracing man, nature, and divinity, the Egyptians seem to have lived cheerfully and reasonably well. The land was very fertile and there was abundance of duck, geese, and other birds in the swamps and reed beds, of fish in the river. The delicate reliefs and paintings on the walls of tombs give us the most detailed and exquisite recollections of this rural life. They show light wooden ploughs drawn by donkeys or oxen at work on the new soil; sowers swinging to and fro across the fields confident that the scattered seed will bring a good harvest; lines of reapers cutting in unison while a piper plays the tune; girls bringing out meals for the menfolk with jokes and banter (these last written in above the heads of the figures as in a strip cartoon); herds of cattle led to pasture near the river edge; fowlers striding through the lotus blossoms holding brace of wild duck, still warm and swinging softly by the necks. Perhaps hippopotamus might get in and destroy a crop, or tax-gatherers demand more than the peasant had to give, but with god on the throne and his previous incarnations safe in their tombs and their immortality, Egyptian life went surely on, with purpose provided by its very order and endurance.

It shows a blind prejudice for historians reared in the restless progress-for-progress-sake philosophy of the modern West to accuse Egyptians of failure because their culture remained static. Their proclaimed object was to defeat change; to them all virtue lay in established moral order of *ma'at,* and their success in maintaining it through the millennia is one of the triumphs of mankind. Energy must always oppose restraint, but let no man identify one with failure and the other with success.

It may have been the confidence inspired by the ordered life of the Nile valley and by the harmonious relationship between divinity, man, and nature there established, which enabled the sculptors of the Old Kingdom to look calmly and objectively at their fellows and carve naturalistic portraits showing the individual faulty as he was and yet full of unquestioned worth. I will select the sculpture of the *Village Mayor* as representing the earliest appearance on earth of man's ability to see himself clearly as an individual and yet love what he saw. Nothing comparable to it will be known again before the days of classical humanism in Greece and Rome.

The Sumerians, the most ancient of the civilized peoples known in the Tigris and Euphrates valleys, had an outlook on life and the cosmos in some ways quite unlike that of the Egyptians. From the first moment we can recall something of their thought, we find them a nervous, somewhat tragically-minded people, with none of the confidence in unchanging order of the dwellers by the Nile. They expected catastrophe and upheaval; they saw themselves as pawns of the gods, created to work for them and always at the mercy of their caprice. In a Sumerian creation myth when the god Enlil breaks the earth's crust so that men may sprout like plants, the other gods beg him to divide the new mannikins among them as slaves. Nor did this point of view change in the Two Valleys, for in the later *Epic of Creation* man was brought into being after Marduk had carelessly observed how useful he would be: 'Let him be hardened with the toil of the gods that they may freely breathe.' So it came about that every city and nation in Mesopotamia was regarded as belonging to its gods, their rulers as the stewards of the gods, and all men alike, theoretically equal, as working for the gods.

As in Egypt and always throughout all our human history, the Sumerians' view of the world drew some of its colour from the nature of their land. In the country of the Two Rivers there was no sharply defined, securely enclosed dominion; the valleys were dominated by the great mountains beyond them, the mountains from which the Sumerians may have come, which they made the home of their gods and which inspired the conical constructions of their art. The nearness of the mountains, too, exposed the valleys to violent storms, and the changing courses of the waterways often washed away or stranded their cities; even the annual floods lacked some of the inscrutable regularity of the Nile's. Man was as threatening as nature. Nomadic invaders from the uplands would sweep down the valleys in sudden conquest, sometimes to be submerged, sometimes asserting themselves as the new rulers.

So there was no unity in these Asiatic valleys, and there civilization did not come into being within one vast state, but in many small states each centred on a city: Kish, Erech, Ur, Lagash, Eridu, and many other of the earliest cities had each its own ruler or king and belonged to its own gods. Thus while the sacred cities of Egypt remained of little political importance in the economic life of the people (Memphis, Thebes, and, for its brief peculiar moment, el Amarna, being comparable to our modern ceremonial capitals such as Washington, Ottawa, and Canberra), the cities of Tigris and Euphrates were the true heart and centre of their states. These states were recognised as a human counterpart to the divine cosmic state in which the gods ruled the Universe. In Sumerian cities the small houses with their four or five little rooms spread out round the temples and palaces, forming into blocks that in turn gave shape to crooked streets and winding alleys. Here for the first time in the world were those city ways where men and women were always passing, or stopping to talk, children playing in the dust, laden donkeys trotting by, dogs scavenging, scuffling, and barking at strangers. In these humble quarters, built up piecemeal by the unplanned events of everyday life, were the dark workshops of the craftsmen, the coppersmiths, weavers, shoemakers, potters, and the rest—craftsmen who were not then distinguished from their fellows, the sculptors, goldsmiths, seal-cutters, and workers in mother-of-pearl and lapis lazuli whom we should distinguish as artists. Here and there, probably usually close by the temples and palaces, there must have been the larger houses of the merchants, men who followed the new urban calling of large-scale trade, organizing long and dangerous expeditions to bring back the raw materials needed for the life and adornment of the city. Round all the buildings, public and private, humble and luxurious, went massive walls, defining this fresh-created human world and strengthening the pride and self-awareness of its inhabitants.

Yet although the ancient cities of Asia supported artisans and merchants (the Sumerians had a word for the 'business man'), and these specialists might give much of their lives to their callings, they seem always to have owned and perhaps tilled some land. As for the ordinary citizens, most of them raised food, going out daily through the gates to cultivate their fields or gardens. So, although the city dwellers must have felt remote from the wild nature in the midst of which, not so long before, their ancestors had passed their lives, they were very far from being cut off from nature and its rhythms. This is shown alike in their daily existence, still anxiously concerned with the annual flood, sun, rain, and all the movements of the seasons, and in the gods they served, nearly all of whom came to be identified with the forces of nature.

I have begun to show how in the two lands where civilization was first brought into existence its forms were not the same. Egypt was a huge, predominantly rural kingdom with its own kind of feudalism. Pharaoh was a god, the gods were immanent in nature and Pharaoh's presence among his people ensured a harmony between man, nature, and the divine that gave the Egyptian a marvellous security not only for his person but also for his psyche. Justice was the social aspect of this cosmic harmony, and if the poor or helpless were sometimes misused, as of course they were and have been ever since, they were still confident in the ideal and could appeal to it. As for the seeming outrage and disturbance of the unchanging harmony by death, the Egyptians convinced themselves that it could be mastered, and laboured to secure an immortality which should force death into place in the timeless cycle of existence. Man, like the sun, like the Nile, like the grain of corn, died in order to rise again. For three thousand years, with only two serious upheavals, both caused by assault from outside, the Egyptians maintained their valley kingdom as a perfect expression of their ideal of unchanging order.

In contrast the Sumerians, and the Semitic peoples who mingled with and conquered them, made civilization flower in numbers of separate city states. Their kings and other rulers were not divine, but merely the stewards and servants of the gods. The divine and the human were separate realms, and men could not count on justice from the gods who had made them for their labour. Nor could the gods' slaves expect eternal life. There was no security: disaster and change were certain, and in face of them unquestioning obedience to one's parents, to officials and rulers, to the gods over all was the ideal of conduct for the good citizen. Just as in Egypt, history exemplified, as it also helped to shape, the outlook of the people. Cities rose and fell in perpetual warfare; one line of kings after another won the national hegemony; invasions and conquest shook the whole land again and again.

As the outlook of the two peoples differed and their society took on different shapes, so too, of course, everything that their hands shaped was wholly distinctive. Their simplest tools and utensils, their clothes, ornaments, houses were as distinctive as their imaginative art, where the stiff, staring-eyed, thick-set figures of the Sumerians, impersonal and indeed inhuman, made the sharpest possible contrast with thc naturalism and individuality of the best early Egyptian portraits and with the graceful elegance of their more stylized works. Here in the two earliest civilizations on earth we find already the eternal originality of our kind, the amazing diversity of our inventive imagination. In the five thousand years since these beginnings of our civilized life, every people, every decade of every people, has had its own peculiarity. It is a truth as simple and as wonderful to contemplate as the variety of our faces, the fact that of all the forgotten millions of countenances we have turned briefly to the world there have been no two indistinguishable to the eye of love.

I have made much of these differences to show in what richly various forms the human mind could give birth to civilization. Yet the likenesses strike deeper and are surely more significant. Indeed, how much alike have the patterns of civilized living been at all times. If one looks at the city as perhaps its highest expression do we not everywhere see the temple, the cathedral, the mosque rising in its sacred precincts at the centre of the town, do we not find dedicated men serving it, and somewhere a ruler who is either himself divine or the delegate of divinity? These things are, as usual, evidently designed to meet a need as urgent as the law court, the house of representatives, the market place, walls and gates, which, as the modern rationalist would say, are forced upon us by the necessities of social and economic life.

Yet in fact walls and gates are not so remote in origin from the houses of god. Both are the product of the dark, that is to say irrational side of our being. Warfare came in part from the need for an outlet of the hunter-animal in us, the wonderful imaginative creation of our gods from the ancient furnishings of our unconscious minds with their universal and untiring urge towards religious expression. Certainly the thousands of gods, goddesses, devils, and other divinities set up, named and worshipped during our history are not simply the imaginative projections of the psyche. These soul figures were identified with what men saw and felt in the natural world on which they depended—with sun, moon, and wind, with the seasons and their rituals, with love and fertility, with cruelty and destruction. Then they were further shaped by men's inner desires, by their terrible longing once they had become fully conscious individuals, to feel that higher powers were looking after them on earth and would save them from death. So the magnificent, grotesque pageant of the gods and goddesses of our religious history, from the Mother Goddess first given tangible form in the images carved by Stone Age hunters, to the great monotheistic gods of the surviving high religions of the modern world, has been compounded of the subtle, inextricable mixture of creations of the conscious and unconscious minds working on their inner and outer worlds, and changing with time and history. We can look at it in humility and awe, this endless procession with so many beautiful figures, so many grotesque and evil ones, and behind them at the works man has made in their honour, the temples, shrines, monuments, images, pictures, masks, mitres, and all the other fantastic furnishings of ritual, works of a significance beyond any other human achievement.

Yes, among all the sources from which our religious forms have sprung, the ancient psychological archetypes are no more than one. As our own historians, however, we must not ignore them for it is likely that this common inheritance of all mankind accounts for the strange similarities between the gods and mythologies of different peoples and all ages. Imitation or inheritance may not, for example, explain many appearances of the dying god and his mother. They may be present and seeking expression in us all, universal forms lurking in the hidden mind.

To say our gods have been projections of the psyche is not to call them false. If none can properly be called the one true god, all have had truth for the peoples who created them; further than this we cannot go, for the mystery must remain further beyond our comprehension than the thought of Einstein is to an ant fleeting across his printed page. For the moment it is enough to be thankful for the noble inheritance our faiths have left us, beginning five thousand years ago with the pyramids of the divine Pharaohs and the White Temple at Erech.

Returning again to the peoples of the river valleys, we can see them as the joint founders of civilization, people who, though certainly influencing one another, would have achieved the new complexities of urban life independently, and who in fact gave it birth in different forms and yet with profound underlying similarities. These parallel paths followed by man in Asia and Africa make one wonder whether the emergent forces of consciousness may not everywhere tend to thrust men along comparable ways. This is not to suggest a series of pre-ordained stages of the kind favoured by Marxist historians; yet looking back over the whole of history it is difficult to escape from belief in the reality of a zeitgeist. An age of primitive farming under the sway of the feminine principle, an age of theocratic cities, of philosopher teachers, of rising intellectualism, of machines. Certainly these developments are not inevitable; many peoples would never themselves have left the age of hunting, yet there do seem to be great tides sweeping through mankind by means other than simple diffusion. One test offers itself to historians but not one has had the courage fully to examine it. Those whose scientific curiosity has led them to the ruins of the pre-Columban civilizations of the New World believe them to have flowered into their macabre but magnificent form entirely without influence from the Old World. We have seen how men first peopled the American continent late in the Pleistocene, entering as savages with a poor Stone Age culture. If it is true that these tribes, totally isolated within the American continent, learnt to cultivate maize and potatoes, then advanced to create the marvellous civilizations found in their decadent brilliance by their European discoverers, then surely here is the most convincing proof of similar evolving patterns within the mind of man giving rise to similar cultural forms. For among the Aztecs and Incas we find again the walled cities, dominated by temples and palaces; we find a noble stone architecture, sculpture, wall painting; we find divine kingship, a priesthood with altars and sacrifices; we find pictographic writing and an astronomical calendar. One of the Conquistadors has left this account of the capital of Montezuma's Mexican empire: 'And when we entered the city, the appearance of the palaces in which they lodged us! How spacious and well built they were, of beautiful stonework and cedar-wood, and the wood of a sweet-scented tree, with great rooms and courts! We went to the orchard and the garden . . . and I was never tired of looking at the trees . . . and the paths full of roses and flowers, and the pond of fresh water. Great canoes passed into the garden from the lake outside so that there was no need for the people to land. All was cemented and very splendid with many kinds of stone monuments with pictures on them. . . . I say again, I stood looking and thought that never in the world would there be discovered such lands as these.'

These were scenes very close in spirit to what could have been enjoyed by the banks of the Nile or in the land of the Two Valleys three or four thousand years before; they appeared wonderful but by no means incomprehensibly alien to the explorers from the Old World of the European Renaissance who stumbled upon them so unexpectedly. Montezuma and Cortes could converse like two civilized gentlemen from neighbouring countries. Was this abundant civilization really created by Mongolian peoples who, since entering their lands as savages, had had no word of what other branches of mankind were achieving in the Old World? If so, what tremendous meaning it has in this study of man and the manifestations of consciousness: with the Atlantic and many millennia between them, the enchanted looms and their flashing shuttles could weave patterns most strangely alike.

intellect 7

The steeling of rational thought

Man's body and the structure of his brain had long been as complete as our own, yet when he provided them with monumental cities and a domesticated countryside in which to live, and found a means to fix mutable thoughts, feelings, and knowledge in written signs, he approached very much closer to our own condition as bearers of consciousness. In the five thousand years since the Egyptians and Sumerians gave birth to civilization our kind has brought more and more of the world within the grasp of mind, and has filled the human treasury with a marvellous inheritance of the products of its arts and skills. It has also enriched itself with the knowledge which could only come with living in time—the accumulated experience which is history. Then, too, from the two tiny centres by the Nile and the Euphrates where it first came into being, civilization has been carried about the world, sometimes gradually, sometimes in brilliant outbursts of genius, always until today leaving islands among its swirling currents where peoples continued to live as hunters or primitive farmers, islands where scientific man could return in detached curiosity to learn something at least of the ways of his ancestors.

Nevertheless, in spite of the far greater richness and complexity of the modern world, the state of man's consciousness in the ancient civilizations was not so far from our own. Most of the delights, desires, problems, and anguishes both private and social which are our lot today, occupied the citizens of Memphis and Ur, more acutely those of Thebes and Babylon. The one momentous innovation since that time has been the growth of the rational intellect. The ancient peoples, though in no way more stupid than ourselves, had not yet begun to use the cerebral part of the mind, the last gift of evolution, in cold detachment from the emotions and the imaginative creations gushing up into consciousness from more primitive sources. The rational intellect, man's highest and most dangerous faculty, had to be set free and cultivated before true philosophy, science, and its violent and uncontrollable child, industry, could be brought into the world. The birth of the free intellect and of reason is therefore the one remaining entry of importance which must be added to this chronicle before I can bring it quite up to date.

It is, however, impossible to pass directly to the Greeks and their unique intellectual courage without pausing for a moment among the many adventures and achievements of our kind during the intervening centuries. Especially I want to consider certain patterns in history which came into being with civilization as a result of the nature of human consciousness. It is no intention of mine to write of the Babylonians and Assyrians, of the Medes and Persians, the Hittites, Phoenicians, or the Indo-Europeans. Perhaps it is good just to blow the trumpet of their names, sounds able to summon memories of hanging gardens and winged bulls, of brilliant glazes and exquisite miniatures, of merchant sailors, and galloping horsemen. To think of these peoples reminds one again of man's endless creative fecundity, his restlessness and violence, and also of the rise and fall of cultures.

Any intelligent being from another planet would, I think, be puzzled by two quite opposite ideas to be found in our attempts to reconstruct our own history. Some historians write as though the story of man on earth was a fairly continuous progress, with invention added to invention, idea to idea and, as a result, an ever mounting control and understanding of nature. This has its truth. We know how we have gone from stone through bronze to iron and steel in the stuff of our tools; we know that after the invention of the bow and arrow in the Old Stone Age and weaving and potting in the New, our ancestors added the plough, the wheel, the sail, the working of copper and bronze during the fourth and third millennia B.C.; we know they went from magic and tribal daimons to the worship of high gods, from empirical mathematics and astronomy to all the fine complexities of theoretical science. It is extraordinary, indeed, how tenacious we have been of our skills and knowledge: in spite of our violent and bloody history, in spite of the many times when barbarians have put the civilized, the learned, and skilful to the sword, or neighbouring peoples ruined one another by ceaseless and idiotic warfare, few of the inventions made by men of genius have ever disappeared altogether from the earth; even knowledge and intellectual methods, though they have fluctuated from age to age, have seldom been quite extinguished from the human brain. Somewhere some few individuals kept them alive even through the darkest times. Thus, not only have there been wheeled vehicles on the roads, sailing-ships on the waters for the past five thousand years, but our mathematicians, physicists, astronomers, and surgeons still use knowledge which has been in circulation since it was painfully worked out by the ancient priesthoods.

All these are facts, and may seem to contradict what I have said about the fragility of culture. Yet other historians are able to write our story as though it were composed of a series of disjointed episodes, the perpetual rise and fall of peoples and cultures. And they, too, speak some part of the truth. There is no need to accept Spengler's automatic phases of rise and eclipse, nor Toynbee's twenty-one cultures with their peculiar mechanisms, to be aware of recurrent loss in history as well as continuous gain.

Indeed all of us with any wisdom know that in many of the highest and most precious of human gifts and attributes we today are no more advanced, but indeed often much poorer, than peoples who held the flame of consciousness hundreds or thousands of years before us.

My friend Gordon Childe ended one of his most remarkable books with these sentences. 'Progress is real if discontinuous. The upward curve resolves itself into a series of troughs and crests. But in those domains that archaeology as well as written history can survey, no trough ever declines to the low level of the preceding one; each crest out-tops its last precursor.' They were written before we entered into the shadow of the atom bomb, so I am not blaming the author for over-optimism or failing to allow for the last wave rising to destroy the planet, but I think these sentences do confuse two quite distinct elements in our human faculties: the imaginative and the intellectual.

Professor Childe and those who think like him attach the highest importance to purely intellectual achievements and to the skill and techniques which they control. Here the gain has been continuous. Any reasonably capable student now at college could put the finest Greek mathematician to shame; any schoolchild could outdo the wise men of Sumer and Egypt. It is in the things of the imagination, of the complete psyche, that the spirit bloweth where it listeth. No living artist would dare to claim equality with Mozart, Rembrandt, or Aeschylus; it would be a presumptuous sculptor who was confident of surpassing the masters of the Egyptian Old Kingdom. Great and small, imaginative powers may ebb away, and no effort of will, it seems, can regain them. A small instance may be as apt as a greater one: from Charles the First's to George the Fourth's, there are many fine equestrian statues still standing amid the iron traffic of London, but today no matter how much a sculptor is paid, how excellent his tools and foundry, or how long and minutely he studies men on horseback and the works of his predecessors, we can be sure his labours can only result in an abominable equestrian statue.

Looking again inside the skull at the immediate source of all our abilities and disabilities, it seems evident that while the purely intellectual output of the Cerebrum, which can be exactly stated in words and recorded in writing, is usually maintained and tends to be heightened and refined from generation to generation, creations in which the Old Brain with its emotions and bodily relationships, its power over the unconscious are involved, creations, that is to say of high imagination or sensibility, appear often to wane with the old age of a people as they so commonly do with the old age of an individual artist. And, while one honours the intellectual achievement of our species, it is the works of imagination and feeling that give cultures their distinctive flavour, colour, and form, their power to delight and inspire. It is through them that a people is mainly remembered and judged. In their pure imaginative essence there is no progress in these things; from the age of the cave-paintings to the age of the Impressionists, from the Congo to China, genius has merely flowered and flowered again with all the riotous variety of the garden, while intellectual attainment has gone forward —erratically, but forward.

Yet although history shows beyond doubt that the physical energy and imaginative power of a people may rise and fall with something of the trajectory of a single human life, and although a terrestrial map shows the old areas of civilization now burnt out and the new, untried areas flaring up, as though civilization were like a fire which consumes its substance, it is unwise to force these movements into universal or mechanical patterns. Every individual is born to die, but there is no such certainty in the existence of peoples. So long as there is human life on earth it may always and anywhere flare out with the original and unexpected. Then, too, decay itself has its own peculiar values. Just as ruins can be more lovely, more moving and significant than a building fresh from the masons' hands, so a people obsessed with its own decline and degeneracy may be able to explore and express, as no budding one can, the tragic aspect of humanity, our courage in face of a reasonable, farsighted despair.

Furthermore, because intellect and imagination play upon one another, the development of intellectual power can give imaginative works greater subtlety and penetration. Thus while it would be false to say that the writings of Proust are greater works of art than those of Homer, we need not deny them a subtler, more fully realized knowledge of human beings, their nature and condition; while the animals glowing on the roof and walls of the Lascaux cave are as magnificent as Leonardo's horses and more poetic, the Renaissance master's new knowledge of anatomy, his intellectual apprehension of what lies below the skin, give his work some added meaning and more universal power. So we can hope that so long as we show some piety and honour to the creative mind and do not wantonly destroy it and its accumulated treasures, consciousness is being enriched and heightened even as men and women die, and peoples rise and fall.

It is time to relax from so much formality, and recall that although, as we have seen, civilization first came into being in two distinct forms and has given rise to many unique and vividly individual cultures since, yet even within these individual forms there always exists enormous variety. We speak of twentieth-century England, and even of a Christian country, yet it includes men, institutions, and ideas as various as Bertrand Russell and Archbishop Fisher, Dylan Thomas and Professor Ayer, Winchester scholars and barrow boys, Plymouth Brethren and the Rationalist Press, nuclear fission and praying for rain, myself and yourself. In the United States the diversity of culture is so great that it is astonishing to find any reality in a dominant pattern which can justly be called American. Millions of people in both countries who read their horoscopes in the popular Press and are infinitely ignorant and credulous, certainly come far nearer to their kind in Sumer and Egypt than to the leading minds of their own societies.

Although the ancient cultures were simpler and more consistent, because their peoples had so much less to choose from and be confused by, they still comprised far more various and changing points of view than we usually trouble to imagine.

I want now to give some account of the mental existence of the peoples of the Tigris and Euphrates valleys, both Sumerians and Semites, choosing to do so partly because their history spans the time between the height of the earliest cities and the intellectual adventures of the Greeks and Chinese, partly because it is both deeply moving and relevant to my theme to see the human mind in its first recorded encounter with some of the dragons of existence which beset the road of every individual. These Asian peoples are a better choice than the Egyptians just because they saw life more tragically, were less constant and harmonious. As we have seen, their first reaction to what they found within and without their skulls was to see themselves as the helpless slaves of the gods. Hence they took anything life gave them as a favour, doing what they could with libations of beer and obedience to their commands to win the goodwill of divinities great and small. This point of view which allows us no absolute rights on earth seems to me to be fundamentally the true one for our kind, but then as now men were reluctant to accept it.

Gradually, as within the security of cities individual self-consciousness became keener and society more strongly knit, men began to expect justice as a right, and to feel resentment not only at injustice among their fellows, but at the overwhelming injustice of the human lot. These, the first human beings to live in their own predominantly human world, in total ignorance of the aeons of their lowly animal history stretching back behind them, could find no good reason for death and the sufferings of the virtuous. Hammurabi had caused laws to be lettered on stone, but still the good might not prosper and all men passed away. Always it must be the same. As the individual becomes more sharply conscious of himself, more open to the world and the heights and depths of experience, he suffers more anguish in the face of life's brevity. And the people of the Two Lands did not find much comfort in hopes for a future world.

This timeless anguish of the soul at the prospect of death is wonderfully expressed in the Epic of Gilgamesh, composed, like the Code of Hammurabi, early in the second millennium B.C. The heroic Gilgamesh has accepted the necessity of death on his own behalf, arming himself against it with the hope of winning an immortal name—man's alternative solace to the hope of immortal life and only a little less ancient.

Who, my friend, was ever so exalted
As to rise up to heaven and dwell lastingly with Shamash?
Mere man—his days are numbered,
Whatever he may do, he is but wind.
You are—already now—afraid of death.
Where is the fine strength of your courage?
Let me lead. . . .
And if I fall, I shall have founded fame.
Gilgamesh fell (they will say) in combat with terrible Huwawa.

Yet when at last this beloved friend is indeed killed by the gods, Gilgamesh is frantic with grief:

'My friend, my younger brother—who with me in the foothills
Hunted wild ass, and panther in the plains. . . .
Who with me could do all, who climbed the crags. . . .

"Man the measure of all things:" idealizing humanism

GREEK HEAD

GOTHIC HEAD

". . . man . . . as a transfigured vessel for the grace of God

Now—what sleep is this has seized you?
You have grown dark and cannot hear me.'
Then he covered his friend, as if he were a bride. . . .
His voice roared out—a lion. . . .
A lioness chased from her whelps.
Again and again he turned towards his friend,
Tearing his hair and scattering the locks,
Stripping and flinging down the finery of his body.

Although when after seven days 'a maggot dropped from his nose' Gilgamesh relinquishes his friend's body, he still will not accept death itself and sets out on an arduous quest to find the secret of immortal life. His fellow mortals whom he meets by the way, less heroic, more resigned than he, tell him to accept the fate of all mankind.

'Gilgamesh, whither are you wandering?
Life, which you looked for, you will never find.
For when the gods created man, they let
Death be his share, and life
Withheld in their own hands.
Gilgamesh, fill your belly—
Day and night make merry,
Let days be fully of joy,
Dance and make music day and night.
And wear fresh clothes,
And wash your head and bathe.
Look at the child that is holding your hand,
And let your wife delight in your embrace.
These things alone are the concern of men.

The hero does not heed them, wins the herb of immortality from the deep sea bed, only to lose it at last to a snake.

Then Gilgamesh sat down and wept,
Tears streaming down his cheeks. . . .
'For whose sake has my heart's blood been spent?
I brought no blessing on myself—
I did the serpent underground good service.'

How right that this ancestral epic should end in tragic uncertainty. These people of the Land of the Two Rivers, not long emerged from the mental comforts of the tribe, encountered death as we encounter it, only more nakedly, with less preparation; their hero Gilgamesh displayed all that is noblest in the active aspect of man's response to his predicament. He fought against death, failed, groaned but would not be satisfied or pretend he knew the answer.

How right it is, too, that our new curiosity should have led us back to these river valleys and their mounded cities, allowing us to free from the silt of ages the little clay tablets on which the scribes, perhaps seated cross-legged in the temple precincts below rainless blue Asian skies, had printed their epic of death and immortality. Not long before, this very people had invented the mode of pressing reed-tips thus-and-thus into the soft clay to capture and perpetutate their spoken words, and, behind them, their inward imaginings. Their ingenuity had created writing, our curiosity took us back to read it, and so across the span of nearly four thousand years minds meet, feelings mingle. Perhaps after all Gilgamesh has had success of a kind in his heroic quest.

Far more obviously shocking to man's growing hope of justice than the inevitability of death were those occasions when the obedient man, the man who had observed all the laws of the gods and their human stewards, was yet struck down by illness and misfortune. One forerunner of Job describes how

'The days when gods were worshipped were my heart's delight,
Those when I followed in the train of the goddess were my gain and profit,
Adoration of the king was joy to me,
Music for him a source of pleasure.
And I instructed my estate to observe the ritual of the gods,
I taught my people to revere the names of the goddess.'

Yet in spite of so much righteousness

'Alu-*disease covers my body like a garment*
Sleep in a net enmeshes me. . . .
All day a persecutor chases me,
At night he gives me no respite. . . .
No god came to my aid, or grasped my hand
My goddess did not pity me or succour me.'

In this particular poem of complaint one explanation of the injustice is the lofty one, offered how many times since,

'The thoughts of a god are like deep waters, who could fathom them?
How could mankind, beclouded, comprehend the ways of gods?'

The other is the happy ending, always necessary in popular literature; after all his sufferings the great Marduk gave him back health and happiness according to his deserts. This answer has been yet more frequently repeated than the sterner one—it is to shut one's eyes on what everyone has seen happen, and desperately to proclaim the reliability of divine providence. Neither is quite worthy of the free mind of man.

Today the yearning for justice by right in all aspects of our human life is usually rationalized, yet it remains as when this plaint was uttered. Those who in the United Nations proclaim such Rights of Man as the right to health, food, work, and education are really in their unconscious minds appealing not to governments but to some external sanction and to one quite unrelated to the actual condition of our life in this world. Now that we know of microbes and viruses and how they spread, we no longer blame our enemies or the gods for unjustly striking us down, but we do rationalize our inner conviction of the injustice of such suffering by proclaiming a Right to Health. The gods today are housed in Ministries rather than in temples.

The other possible reaction to the hardness and frequent injustice of our lot was also already well known to the people of these ancient cities. Pessimism, cynicism and a kind of triumphant despair. Admittedly this was, as it still usually is, a mark of a culture in decline, and the expression of it which I am going to quote was uttered in the last millennium before Christ when the Ancient World was breaking down. Still I do not doubt that long before then individual citizens, old or embittered, had known this loss of all faith and value. In this *Dialogue of Pessimism* a master is speaking to his slave, and always after proclaiming his intention to do something good, or at least positive, he then denies the intention as being vain and valuelcss. The slave, the more cynical of the two, does not fail to agree with both confirmation and denial. I will quote only the denials.

'No, slave, I will not love a woman!'
'Love not, my lord, love not!
Woman is a snare, a trap, a pitfall;
Woman is a sharpened iron sword
Which will cut a young man's neck.'

'No, slave, I will not make a libation to my god!'
'Make it not, my lord, make it not!
Teach the god to run after thee like a dog.'

'No, slave, I will not gives alms to my land!'
'Do it not, my lord, do it not!
Mount thou upon the ruined mounds of ancient cities,
Beholding the skulls of those of earlier and later times.
Who is the evildoer, who is the benefactor?'

There could hardly be a better evocation of both psychical and physical decay than this verse; already cities were ruined mounds, and man, having denied love, faith, and morality, is heavy with the death wish:

'Slave, agree with me!' 'Yes, my lord, yes!'
'Now then, what is good?
To break my neck and thy neck,
To fall into the river—that is good!'

I have quoted from these tablets partly to reveal the many and contrary ideas flooding through men's minds in any age, partly to show how in spite of differences of belief, knowledge, language, and all the outward forms of civilization, men always share enough in common both within themselves and in the inevitable events of their lives to bind them together through time in a community of experience. Perhaps, too, I wanted to make these pioneers of civilization recall for us something of the world in which they lived—hunting wild ass in the foothills, panther on the plains, climbing crags, walking in religious processions, dancing, making music, wearing fine clothes, suffering sickness and insomnia, making love, taking a child by the hand, mourning. After a million years of meeting men only through their bones, stones, and potsherds, it is good to hear them speak.

This literature, with its kaleidoscopic play of ideas and feelings, is already able to prove how in the alleys, market-places, law-courts, and temple precincts of the earliest cities, men were being forced into a far sharper consciousness of individuality than they had known in village, farms, and hunting ways. It became keener when the first upward thrust of civilization was over and its inevitable problems and strains made themselves felt. From their economic nature, the urban cultures found themselves involved in imperialism. For the first time we find one people not merely conquering another (this had been going on at least since the extinction of the Neanderthalers) but deliberately ruling them from without. Here, then, was abundant opportunity to be forced into wider doubt and understanding through both conflict and contact with peoples of other races and cultures. Perhaps, then, it is to be expected that it is in the second millennium, the time when widespread imperialism first appeared among men, that we begin to meet with individual personalities strong enough to raise their heads above the main flow of history.

Amenhotep IV, since we recalled his existence not very long ago, has often been hailed as the first historical individual and the first monotheist. He might also be called the first Romantic. There must have been thousands of personalities equally strong before his time, but they had no means of attracting the attention of posterity. Among those who had, Amenhotep's remarkable kinswoman Queen Hatshepsut might well rival him in the field for historical individuality. It was no ordinary woman who could contrive to occupy a throne intended for men only, who could be shown in her monuments wearing male dress and an artificial beard, and prove herself able to rule with the creative success to be shown by so high a proportion of queens in the subsequent history of mankind. Still, beyond doubt, Amenhotep, this attractively ugly young man with a Syrian mother and a beautiful wife, is a potent enough figure to demand fair place in any chronicle of man.

What he achieved has now been brought to the memory of most of us. He was the hub of one of the most perfect and intensely conservative systems ever created by any society, yet, temporarily, he changed its course. True he was a god, but it is hard for us now to imagine what that means to a man. He certainly acted with godlike might. Defying the enormous authority of tradition, he set aside the ancient pantheon, outraging the priests of the then dominant Amon; he quitted Thebes to build a new sacred capital hundreds of miles away on the desert edge at el Amarna; and, in proclaiming Aten, the sun's disc, as the sole god and himself as his prophet, he changed not only his name to Akhenaten, but the whole concept of Egyptian kingship. The worship of Aten was to symbolize the union of all the peoples of the empire under Pharaoh; other sacred cities were built for him to the north and south—in Syria and Nubia. He was the life-giving god, the god with warming hands, portrayed as the solar disc with either life symbols or little hands at the end of its extended rays. His worship was an affirmation of the joy of life, a denial of its dark side and of all those chthonic forces represented in the cult of Isis and Osiris. Such was the ideal of the life in which Akhenaten, Nefertiti, and their seven daughters led their court in the palace at Akhetaten where the very floors were brilliant with frescoes of the flowers and creatures of the Nile.

Akhenaten's hymn to Aten is among the masterpieces of ancient literature, and it reveals him as conceiving not only one god, but also its inevitable counterpart—the unity of mankind.

How manifold are your works!
They are hidden before us,
O sole god whose power no other possesses.
You created the earth according to your heart
While you were yet alone:
Men, all cattle large and small,
All that are upon earth,
That go about upon feet;

All that are on high,
That fly with wings.
The foreign countries, Syria and Kush
The land of Egypt;
You set everyman in his place.

Here, certainly, is a view of wider horizons both in heaven and on earth. Peoples, at a time when they were increasingly diverse, were recognized as being of one kind, and divinity, whether by the banishment or amalgamation of other gods, as a single being. Monotheism was a conception widely taking possession of men's minds at this time, long before it came to the Hebrews. In truth, the significance of the Hebrew's idea of divinity was not so much that it was monotheistic, but that it was taken out of nature. God no longer immanent in nature but its ruler and creator. Centuries before Moses recognized Yahweh as the god of Judah the Babylonians sang of their sun god:

The mighty hills are surrounded by thy glory,
The flat lands are filled with thy brightness,
Thou hast power over the mountains, and lookest over the earth;
Thou dost hang up the hems of the land in the innermost part of heaven.
The men of the lands, thou watchest over them all. . . .
What places are not warmed by the beams of thy light?
Thou who lightest the darkness and brightenest the gloom,
Who puttest to flight the darkness and givest light to the wide earth.

Perhaps after all the coming of the idea of monotheism is not very important. Gods spring from the sense of the numinous which all the religious discover in themselves. Always in reality they worship *their* god, *their* crystallization of the numinous. The form which it takes must depend on the history of the individual and of his time. It is affected, too, by the persistent desire of man (here to be distinguished from woman) to use his intellect to rationalize what should never be rationalized—his intuitions of holiness. That is why the whole character of an established religion changes with history, being shaped by peoples more than it shapes them. Even the concept of the single god is never stable. Christianity, and especially Roman Catholicism, shows how readily the sense of deity can simultaneously focus into one or radiate into many—Father, Son, and Holy Ghost; the Mother of God; the patron Saint. In Protestant minds, where the hand of the intellect is heavy, the numinous tends to be banished altogether, and an ethic to take its place.

Akhenaten was at the centre of a wide empire, he could envisage 'the earth' even though he did not know its substantial form; he knew the people of 'the foreign countries' as being akin to those 'of the land of Egypt'. Furthermore, he himself had a strong personality, a most powerful imagination; no wonder god for him was a supreme god.

Yet what remains most truly alive of Akhenaten is not his will or power but the tender intimacy of his family life held for us in paint and stone by the artists whom he set free from the narrow bonds of convention. Probably artists were more honoured at his court, more clearly recognized for their imaginative power, the traffic with the unconscious which distinguishes them from even the finest craftsmen, than ever before, or for long afterwards. We know by name some of the men who worked at Akhetaten; there was Bek the chief sculptor, and another, Tutmosis, in whose studio were found not only the famous head of Queen Nefertiti, but also naturalistic plaster casts of human faces, some of them, it seems, life and death masks. In response to freedom, recognition, and the atmosphere of the Court which seems to have been so full of the joy of life, these artists left for posterity studies of the Pharaoh and his queen embracing one another and dandling their daughters, kissing while out driving, exchanging a flower, all with a liveliness, a sense of warm curving flesh altogether lacking in the cool, impersonal dignity of the traditional forms. The feminine charm and feeling they put into the portrait head of the lovely Nefertiti has carried copies of it into thousands of little modern houses all over the world. When I was in Hitler's Berlin I spent an hour or so in the museum among the collections from el Amarna, and was particularly delighted by a sculptured fragment of two hands, softly holding one another, and surely those of Egypt and his wife. Looking back now on this, my only visit to Berlin, while the rest of the city has blurred to a general impression of dead pretension, these two hands, palm to palm, still appear before me, a touch of tenderness immortalized in fine crystalline stone. So, through the power of art to set time aside, I came back from Nazi Germany with memories of two palms that touched in love over three thousand years ago by the river Nile.

During the last millennium before Christ the ancient world, the outcome of man's first great feat of civilization, everywhere came to an end. Warfare, decay, change of character destroyed the old forms. 'To break my neck and thy neck, to fall into the river—that is good.' Yet even while the ancient world was foundering, with the end of the long trajectory of Egyptian culture clashing against the short sharp rise of Assyria, an altogether new phase in the development of human consciousness was beginning. It is just because the stuff of decay may so often fertilize a new crop that closed systems such as Toynbee's can be quite misleading. During the second and third quarters of the last millennium B.C. an extraordinary number of great men were born into the world, thinkers and teachers who in most various ways used their intellects in an endeavour to relate men to the universe not by means of myth and ritual but by reason and morality.

Beginning with the Hebrew prophets Amos and Isaiah, there followed Zoroaster, Buddha, Lao-Tsze, Confucius, the Ionian Greeks, Pythagoras, and Socrates, all born within three centuries. It is an astonishing growth, and one that sprang up along the whole length of the literate cultures which now stretched across the Old World from the Atlantic to the Pacific. One can explain it as an awakening caused by the collapse of the old theocracies and the fading from men's minds of the myths which had sustained them; one can say there may have been some traffic between all the different areas of thought—as there certainly came to be between several of them. But also, if one believes, as I do, that the development of consciousness on this earth is related to cosmic processes beyond our ken, then it is tempting to see this appearance of thinkers in Greece, Palestine, Persia, India, and China as a further stage of unfolding to which mind and brain had by now won their way. What I am sure is *not* the explanation is the discovery of iron-smelting, the invention of coinage and phonetic alphabets, which the materialists put forward as the explanation of this sudden intellectual outburst. Such people will always confuse what makes a development possible or easier with what causes it. These material aids to democracy—making good tools cheaper, reading and writing easier, and the exchange of goods more free, certainly facilitated the cultivation of mind by all manner of men, ending the priestly monopoly. But it did no more, and if one is inclined to think that the abstract thought of the Greeks could not have been set down intelligibly if the Phoenicians had not perfected an alphabet just in time, one should remember that Oriental philosophers had to work with a script at least as complicated and difficult to master as cuneiform or hieroglyphics. However, history is not a science even if some of these materialists think it is, so on no account should I object to their stating their own point of view. No interpretation of history is finally or altogether true, and there is none which does not illumine some small part of the mystery of our evolution—even if it consists in denying the existence of any mystery. Better to say birds sing because they have a syrinx than to imagine they keep flutes tucked under their wings.

It is profoundly stirring to think of these great men, many of them on earth at the same time, the same day's sun greeting them as it advanced from Orient to Occident. Say, perhaps a day in 525, when the sun first woke old Lao Tsze and young Confucius, and sent the old man to his work among the archives at the Court of Chow or to meditation on the Tao, while somewhere in Shantung Confucius, already in his mid-twenties far advanced in his pursuit of wisdom, put on the mourning clothes he was wearing for his beloved mother and went out to teach his disciples. Then, as the earth turned and Benares came into the sun's light, dawn would find Siddhattha Gautama, the Buddha, with his days of pleasure as a Rajah's son set sternly behind him, rising from some comfortless bed and setting out with his begging bowl, to spread the enlightenment which had come to him seven years before under the Bo tree. Some hours later the sun would rise on the Ionian coast of Asia Minor lighting up the comfortable homes of the Greek natural philosophers of the school of Thales, public and professional men who, rather than turn their eyes inward towards their own psyche, looked out towards a world they believed to be an intelligible whole, and used senses and intellect in an effort to apprehend and order it. Men who, rather than seek understanding under a Bo tree, would seek to understand the tree itself. Of this school, Anaximander had already by his study of animals and fishes gained at least a hazy idea of evolution, while that very morning Xenophanes might be going out to collect fossils whose meaning as marks of former life he understood—probably the first man on earth to recall something of the events with which this book begins. Heracleitus, the proud aristocrat, would stay indoors in his study, for his intellect, leading him to think of existence as perpetual change and process rather than as various being, was turning him towards metaphysics and away from the observation of nature. Westernmost, and therefore last of all, Pythagoras would wake up at Crotona, the Greek colony in southern Italy where he had recently fled from his island home in Samos; breaking fast with the members of the mystical brotherhood he had gathered round him, he may perhaps have spent the morning in a severe exercise of pure intellect, wrestling with some part of the theory of numbers which he believed could explain the nature of the world.

As a stage in the history of consciousness, this great rousing of mind right across the Old World is of fascinating significance. As a matter of general principle it illustrates the interplay between mankind and the individual; evidently there was something either about the condition of the age or the phase of human development which lay behind this unique mental flowering, yet it was initiated in the brains of a score of men, each distinctively himself, leading his own life and allowing it to colour his thought. As a matter of particular history it is no less significant. The thinkers of this age led the way which the cultures of their peoples were to follow down to the present time, and already, though clearly all were affected by some common awakening of intellectual power, the sages of the East and the western philosophers had chosen different roads.

Although in centuries to come China was to know creeds both of social morality and of social realism stark enough to please Machiavelli or modern totalitarian bosses, the cultivation of consciousness was predominantly subjective, a turning inwards to secure good states of psychic being for the individual soul, a purpose which was pursued through psychological methods both subtle and arduous. In the West, though there, too, exceptions were many, the cultivation of consciousness was predominantly concerned to turn it outwards, treating earth and the heavens, society, then man himself as objects to be understood, mastered, and finally exploited. Thus the East sought a state of being, and honoured the feminine principle in intuitive powers of mind; the West pursued knowing and enthroned the intellect and its masculine principle. Western man used the might of the Cerebrum to conquer the outer world; Eastern man lived inside the skull, harmonizing the life of Old Brain and New, learning to control the strange, hidden world of the psyche. The West in its intellectual pride set up man as the measure of all things, and in its art portrayed him alone and either heroically or with idealized naturalism; intuitively, out of the corner of the eye, the East saw man in modest harmony with nature and in its art portrayed him as a part of landscape, and often somewhat comical. It also used its delicately schooled sensibilities to portray plants and flowers, beasts, birds, fishes, and insects with an expressiveness never to be equalled, generation after generation of artists repeating the same subjects, intensifying and purifying them with a humility of spirit remote from the bold, progressive, exploring spirit of their fellows in the West. There could be no finer historical symbol of the two ways than that Alexander should have set out to conquer the world, while the Chinese enclosed themselves behind their Great Wall.

The causes for this wide divergence of ideal must be as complicated and confused as my statement of them has been oversimplified. I would again pick out only one—the perennial influence of land upon people. The brilliantly clear days and nights of Greece, the small, compact, and relatively prosperous communities, harbours crowded with sailors of a score of lands, open seaways always near at hand and leading to the fertile, lightly populated lands of barbarian neighbours, must all have served to draw out psychic energy with promise of worlds to conquer. The huge land masses of the Orient with their heat and dust, the terrible familiarity with teeming life and monotonous death, would have made men glad to escape from the outer to the inner world.

There now I must leave the Orientals, walled in, conservative, successfully cultivating and practising their ideal, until suddenly we meet them face to face in the present, forcing ourselves into their static world, and finding at last that while they are now ready to seize upon the products of our extraverted energy, we begin to recognize our need for their ancient psychological wisdom.

With the Greeks and their new conception of the universe as an intelligibly ordered whole, the human mind at last began to apprehend the physical nature of the planet on which it had evolved. The recollection of Sumerian and Babylonian poetry has shown how these pioneers of civilization became conscious of their human predicament with its injustice and death, but for them the earth and its surroundings were beautifully obscured in myth. Now the Hellenistic Greeks carried forward the scientific observation of their surroundings begun by the Ionians. Alexandria became the cerebral centre of mankind, the place where the new thinkers could come in contact with one another and also with the ancient inheritance from Egypt and Babylonia. So mind, which had hitherto been related to the outer world mainly through the senses, now became more widely related through the apprehensions of pure thought. For it is a paradox in human affairs that while the heightening of consciousness, the sharpening of intellect, have made us more and more agonizingly aware of our isolation from nature they have in truth served to unite us with wider and wider ranges of the universe. The curious mind setting out on its intrepid exploration of the cosmos unites all its conquests in man's being.

Alexandria, then, became the base from which the greatest mental explorations were launched. Already the simpler physical journeys of soldiers and merchants had extended the known surface of the earth to include much of Europe, Asia, and the fringes of Africa; but now mind, leaping far beyond the discoveries of everyday experience and common sense, recognized this surface to be that of a sphere, estimated the sphere with some accuracy and divided it into degrees with the determination of a child eating an orange. These lines of latitude and longitude, the imagined lines which we now see inscribed upon all maps and globes, symbolize the first stages of man's mental grip upon the planet. The ancient realm of the Earth Mother had been secured in a mathematical mesh.

Nor was thought earth-bound. It went out against those venerable divinities the Sun and Moon, estimating their girths and distance from the earth. It was a tremendous attack on common sense—that is to say upon the obvious interpretation of the message brought by the senses to the brain—when intellect declared the familiar flat-seeming earth to be a ball. It was an emotional shock to know that mental callipers were being applied to the heavenly bodies. The supreme assault on common sense, piety, and human self-regard was ventured upon at this time only to be relinquished. Two thousand two hundred years ago the intellectual powers developed by Aristarchus of Samos enabled him to suggest that the earth went round the sun, but he was contradicted in scientific argument by his colleagues, and also denounced as impious by philosophers in whose brains thought moved in more traditional channels. This particular physical fact was, therefore, denied mental existence, so far at any rate as this earth is concerned, for another seventeen centuries, and for so long was man saved from knowing (a knowledge which was to affect his consciousness) that his home was not at the centre even of one small planetary system.

I cannot omit Athens from this chronicle, so much has it become a symbol of the Western ideal. Yet from the point of view of the intellect surveying and penetrating the physical surroundings into which it was born, Athens did less than the Ionian or Hellenistic Greeks. In approaching the physical world its thinkers were less fearless in pursuit of truth. Nevertheless Socrates for all his sophistry makes a splendid personification of the coming age of intellect. Plato and Aristotle have had a tremendous power in shaping the European mind both Christian and other, and still, though their influence wanes, help to shape it. Is not my son even now toiling to master their very words—and some part at least of their meaning? Was not the authority of Aristotle so great in the Middle Ages that even on the subject of nature men would rather believe him than consult nature herself.

But even beyond this intellectual honour, Athens lives on for us as an expression of what man can achieve at his best, when body, imagination, and intellect are all free and in harmony. We think of it as a beautiful city, enriched by its artists, yet honouring its gods, listening to its philosophers and poets, yet glorying in bodily beauty and strength. Above all we think of it as the centre of a state where all the citizens ruled themselves, and democracy, for all its follies and dangers, can do much to strengthen and liberate the individual mind. Certainly Athens has become something of a dream image for Western man, and if it is in many ways false and has led to illusions, yet it is no less precious as a symbol, and one which should always give strength while the human mind lives in freedom.

These centuries of Greek culture, when the cerebral intellect of man came fully into its own, discovering, and indeed youthfully over-estimating its power, proved fertile for the growth of philosophies. The intellect, turning both inward in abstract reasoning and outward towards the infinite complexity of the world, constructed many theoretical systems to explain how man and universe came into being, what their purpose might be and the nature of the relationship between them. The thinkers were like clever children running to play with new toys, and they built many lovely or ingenious intellectual constructions with them. The mistake then, as now, was to take them too seriously, to believe that one or another expressed some absolute and final truth. This they can never do; philosophy and theology are noble masculine exercises which save the mind from stiffness and sloth.

No one ever thought the rival truths of Austen, Tolstoi, or Proust called for hemlock, faggots, or war, nor should those of philosophers and theologians.

One of the constructions of this time, of which Plato was the chief architect, was the notion of dividing all things into two—reality and appearance, soul and body, this world and the next, the greater good lying always in the one out of the pair which could be apprehended by the mind but not the senses—the well-known dualism which in one way and another has brought so much misery and frustration, wasted such a world of delight, for all those in the West who inherited and accepted it. Yet Plato himself, living in an age of abounding life and treading the way of the golden mean, did not so divide and ruin life and his experience of it. How beautifully, indeed, he reconciles the two sides of his dualism:

> Had we never seen the stars, and the sun, and the heaven, none of the words which we have spoken about the universe would ever have been uttered. But now the sight of day and night, and the months and the revolution of the years, have created number, and have given us a conception of time; and the power of inquiring about the nature of the universe; and from this source we have derived philosophy, than which no greater good ever was or will be given by the gods to mortal man.

It was of course in Christianity that this dualism found its strength to drive mankind so far in both exaltation and misery, and in Christianity Plato's philosophy was exaggerated by the outlook of a people whose ideals were remote indeed from the golden mean. I have spoken many times of the colour lent by a land to the mind of its people, but with the Hebrews it was rather the lack of a secure homeland which coloured their thought. With a background of pastoral life and its rigid, patriarchal authority, a proud and gifted people who had to take their land as invaders, who were ground between two vastly stronger neighbours and had even known captivity among them, could not fail to think violently in black and white, to call up the force of the masculine principle to enforce what could readily become a harsh and intolerant morality. Furthermore their early nomadism, followed by an insecure relation to their land, had encouraged the Hebrews to lift god out of nature and set him above it to fulfil their new myth—the myth of the Will of God. So when in Christianity Hebrew faith and morality came together with Greek philosophy it was inevitable that the supposedly evil part of the dualism, the whole world of the senses, would be thrown down and mercilessly chastized.

Perhaps even if Hebrew and Greek had never come together in Paul and his successors in the Christian Church, division was bound at this time to rend the human psyche. After tremendous initial successes, the intellect had over-estimated its capacity; even Plato grew embittered when he saw his carefully weighed theories for the perfect state fail miserably in the face of the overwhelming extravagance and power of irrational life. Perhaps, then, it was certain to turn against the body and the senses, separating the soul and setting it above and against the body, just as the Hebrews had separated god from nature.

Causes were many, and the thing happened. After so huge a span of time during which body and psyche evolved together in a single process, the arrogant young intellect tried to put them asunder. Whatever may be our understanding of the meaning of evolution, I hope that no one who has read this book with sympathy can doubt that man and his psyche are at one, united in holy wedlock, and cannot be divided any more than the New Brain can be divided from the Old, or the brain as a whole from the nervous system and the body in which it lies enfleshed.

The Romans, as the conquerors and disciples of the Greeks, for all their military and legal gifts, are significant in this history mainly for uniting the Western world and opening its roads to Christianity. Nevertheless they must also be remembered here for greatly extending the areas of civilization across the surface of the earth. At about the time when on the other side of the Atlantic men were at last creating high civilization in the New World, the irresistible discipline and intellectual control of the Roman legions were taking literacy and something at least of urban life to the extremities of Europe. Nowhere do we get a better instance of the imposition of intellectual upon intuitive and unconscious forms. Roman roads cutting across the wilderness and displacing Celtic trackways; Roman houses, rectangular and planned, displacing rough Celtic huts; Roman art, now often mere lifeless repetition, displacing the brilliant, spontaneous art of the barbarians. The Celts proved such apt pupils of all that was good and bad in the classical civilizations imposed upon them that very soon they were contributing able brains to the resources of the Empire. Even now the minds of those peoples who kept their independence beyond the Roman *limes* to the west and north have a different cast from those who lived within them. A difference which has been of great benefit to both.

Yet the achievement of the Romans, as the spreaders of urban civilization, was to prove of secondary importance beside their provision of a stout framework for Christendom. It would be vain and indeed ridiculous for me to attempt to argue for or against the truths of Christianity, for its truth lies with the individual and in the living fulfilment of the myth. It is one of man's noblest efforts to express his intuitions of realities far beyond his comprehension. I will simply state how in the disillusion and moral weakening of the later Empire, the mystery religion, with its trailing clouds of Greek and Jewish thought, which had been bringing comfort and the promise of immortality to slaves and poor men, became so powerful as to prove irresistible to the divine Emperor himself. One can say either that Christianity defeated the imperial power or that the imperial power captured Christianity. Although the secular state remained more distinct, the new situation strangely recalls the ancient theocracies; indeed, Byzantium had much in common with Sumeria and Babylonia. In the west the barbarian invaders, themselves still living by myth, were civilized by Christianity and in return poured their youthful imaginative and bodily energy into their new faith, creating some of the most spiritual art and sublime architecture man has ever raised out of the stone and clay of earth.

For the purposes of this chronicle the fundamental meaning of the victory of Christianity in the western half of the Old World is that the myth-making powers of the human mind had found renewed life and power, while the career of the rational intellect, as the instrument of a free and fearless curiosity, was interrupted. We can be thankful it was so interrupted, for had the intellect gone steadily forward from its Greek beginnings to the developments which were to follow the Renaissance without this period of healing by myth and imaginative achievement, our predicament in any imaginable 'now' might be bleak indeed. Nevertheless the dualism which had unhappily been incorporated in Christianity damaged the psyche, leading to the attempted suppression of all those parts nourished by the senses and bodily life, and hence to the eruption of cruelty, violence, eroticism, and witchcraft and the most hideous images of hell. That particular expression of duality which inspired the idea of this world and the next did further mischief by intensifying Western man's terrible awareness of linear time, sending him hurrying through his three score years and ten to reach a bliss lying always in the future. It is conspicuous how, in spite of many weaknesses, the Chinese religious succeeded far better than the Christians in translating their values into life; the followers of the avowed religion of love fought—and what is more gave conscious honour to fighters—persecuted, martyred, in imagination joyfully pitchforked enemies into eternal agonies. The wilderness which men brought with them inside the walls of civilization grew more than ever wild and uncontrollable when hated and denied.

We can be thankful for Christendom, yet still recognize it as an interruption in a dominant trend in the evolution of mind, and so be equally thankful that, by what seems an act of historical providence, the Arabs kept alive and developed the intellectual achievements of the Greeks during the Middle Ages, never allowing their gains to be lost from the storehouse of the human brain. So the material of knowledge was there for Europe when after a thousand years of inspiration by the Christian myth men again sharpened their rational curiosity, turned it upon the natural world and set the Renaissance sweeping through the European mind. Once again there were many who saw man as the measure of all things; again there were artists to portray him either in his self-idealizing confidence and pride, or, quite simply, as the creature he appeared to be and not as a transfigured vessel for the grace of god. And once again while the intellect set off on a thousand brave adventures, so also simple men in ships set sail from Europe to bring new continents within the realm of the coherently known. Reaching America, Europeans encountered branches of their species who had been cut off from the Old World for more than ten thousand years. Intolerance made the reunion treacherous and bloody, yet this encounter with unknown races both civilized and savage soon served to sharpen curiosity and broaden understanding. Surprisingly soon after our second discovery that we were the inhabitants of a globe, its principal lands and oceans became known. Man had grasped the physical facts of his earth.

If Socrates and his friends make a symbol for the first maturity of intellect, Copernicus, Columbus, and Leonardo da Vinci are three great contemporaries who can symbolize its renaissance. With their discoveries, inventions, and imaginative foresights they represent the full dawn of our modern world.

a myth for the future 8

There are certain perspective figures, often described as optical illusions, which may first appear to represent solid, projecting forms, but which suddenly, and usually to the observer's astonishment, change into hollow recesses. When my mind has been dwelling in the shadowy aeons of time traversed in this book, I find I experience just such a startling transformation of vision when I look at other human beings, or think about myself. One moment I see them as everyday fellow men going about their familiar affairs, perhaps people I have known all their lives, and certainly individuals who have carried their own particular bodies, with names attached, through the ordinary or extraordinary events of their own lives. I can imagine myself in just the same matter-of-fact way. Then I look or think again and find that we have all of us switched from this familiar appearance and now instead appear as part of some vast, super-personal process, a process which started with bare rocks and empty seas and has now become this concourse of humanity, this realm of living consciousness, pulsating over all the earth in our two and a half thousand million brains.

As with the optical illusion, either view of the picture is equally correct as a version of reality. The vast process is expressed entirely in the individual lives of each one of us, its overwhelming richness being no more than the total of their small gifts; the individual life draws significance and completeness from its place, humble or exalted, within this great becoming. What, however, is a dangerously wrong view of the picture is to see the procession as leading to some promised goal, some glorious apotheosis in future time. Every moment in the process has its own incomparable value; we do not regard a young oak as inferior to a grown one, or a child to an adult. This false view of a progress towards a promised land has been the curse of Western man, whether he be a Christian hurrying through his life on earth towards a future heaven, or a Marxist materialist wading through blood and tears to attain heaven on earth in five years' time.

While there is no goal to which we are progressing, as though passing through a corridor to reach a room, there is, I believe, an all-pervading and transcendent significance in human evolution which we now know enough of the past to comprehend. This is the bringing into being, the heightening, and the intensifying of our consciousness through creative experience at every level of existence. I read our history in this sense and am convinced all value should be related to it. Thus our supreme duty as a kind is to use our individual lives to extend and enrich experience by all the many means which have been made available to us since we became men. The greatest contributions which we are empowered to make, art, mystical experience, and all the fields of pure thought, are limited to a few among millions, but all true experience and all active living have their own value, and help, too, to nourish and support the creative powers of the most gifted. Often those men of genius and psychical power who win fresh territory in the heights and depths of human experience must themselves suffer Promethean torments. Yet this image is not quite the true one for what I am trying to express. Prometheus stole fire from the gods, that is to say brought knowledge or inspiration from higher realms of being down to man, whereas to me it seems we ourselves at our highest are part of those realms, even though a humble part, and contribute to their being and becoming.

If this is the magnetic centre of all our human value then morality should always be directed towards it. Good is all that helps to forward the development of consciousness and experience, evil all that tries to destroy it. Yet these poles of love and hate, of good and evil are necessary to one another even as day cannot be day without night's darkness.

In this chronicle I have said little about morality because most of it is, and should be, transitory—local and topical agreements within societies which should be adjusted to the changes of time. Any ultimate morality must, evidently, relate only to the supreme values. Whatever we have pretended as members of society we have in truth always recognized this, believing in our hearts the men who broke the socially agreed rules, but were full of a rich experience of life or of creative power, to be more valuable, more deserving of our honour, than the spiritless conformers.

If we feel confident of anything in the modern world which has grown out of the Renaissance, it is that we have gone astray. That pride of man in his own power and glory which we can see burning in so many Renaissance portraits has fallen to ash. The confidence in human progress towards betterment which followed in the nineteenth century has fallen after it. At the end of its long evolution the human backbone seems for the present to have lost the stiffness of pride and of confident morality and yet cannot bow in convinced submission before god. Many even of our leaders are turning to dogmatic faiths for support, surrendering our hard-won freedom of thought for a discipline more therapeutic than truly religious. Artists have shown our loss of confidence in ourselves by becoming unable to portray men in their full humanity. Afraid to claim the qualities of spirit, mind, and heart which their predecessors showed in the terms of Christian humility or humanist pride, they have escaped into noncommittal abstract forms.

Now we are full of guilt, despair, and cruelty, all darkened by contrast with our previous rationalistic optimism. We might reassure ourselves a little by recalling how men have always been going wrong, how indeed this was formerly taken for granted as the condition proper to humanity. There have been scores of times, too, when the world must have appeared as disastrous to thinking men as it does today. Dimly, perhaps, to the Neanderthalers when they knew themselves to be doomed; to the Egyptians when Asiatics conquered them and disturbed their faith in *ma'at;* to the Athenians after the Peloponnesian war; to the Romans as their Empire collapsed. The security and hopefulness of the Western world at the time of Queen Victoria's death was quite exceptional and made the four walls of our humanity appear unrealistically solid. Our failures will perhaps appear less fearful, and less shameful too, if we think of history not in centuries or millennia but with the time scale of this book, reflecting upon our origins and accepting our ignorance.

Here then is a handful of comfort, but plainly we cannot save ourselves merely by recognizing pain and insecurity to be our native lot. Besides, we all know that the present speed of change and the terrible forces our cleverness has put into our unworthy hands justify an altogether new sense of crisis. What has gone wrong during the last four hundred years?

The answer can be found along two lines of thought, both really representing aspects of a single process, but which our mental habits oblige us to divide. One refers to life outside our skulls, the other to life within them. I will begin with our life in the external world.

For some time after the Renaissance thinkers had taken up the strands of scientific observation left so long before by the Ionian and Hellenistic Greeks, they too remained pure theorists, seekers after knowledge and truth for their own sake. It was so when Copernicus revived Aristarchus's discovery that earth was the sun's satellite; it was so when Galileo was threatened with torture by the Inquisition for having supported the Copernican view which was 'absurd in philosophy and formally heretical, because expressly contrary to Holy Scripture'. It was so for Newton and the first half-century or more of the life of the Royal Society of London. But gradually during the Age of Reason when in Augustan calm the intellect appeared to be as firmly in control as it did to the Heretics before 1914, men began to apply scientific methods for practical ends, generally for the greater production of goods and the speeding of transport. When the unconscious forces of the mind gushed up, after long suppression, in the Romantic movement, and this same impulse coupled with liberal and revolutionary thoughts overthrew the old order and brought power to the practical, industrious, and mercenary middle classes, man plunged along the way to industrialism with as little deliberate intention as he had known when he became a farmer, or committed himself to living in cities.

As a hunter he had been a robber of nature, but only as one among the rest of the animals, with cunning in place of strength or speed. Then for six thousand years he had, on some parts at least of the earth's surface, been a cultivator and improver of nature, and had interspersed among the beauties of wild scenery wide stretches of the other kind of beauty which goes

RENAISSANCE MAN IN HIS CONFIDENT PRIDE

". . . our loss of confidence in ourselves . . ."

HUMAN FIGURE: HENRY MOORE

with a man-made landscape. He had, it is true, cut forests, taken from the earth some metallic minerals, increasing quantities of coal and stone, and all he could find of substances both rare and attractive to the eye—amber, gold, and precious stones. But numbers were few, mechanical devices to magnify human muscle not over-powerful, and the greater part of what was taken from the earth was used to give expression to imaginative forms themselves springing from the unconscious mind and therefore in harmony with nature. No one, for instance, can look at Gothic architecture without responding to it as a superb creation of nature heightened and given spiritual form through human imagination and intuitions of divinity.

I have written in *A Land* of the devastation our kind has worked upon earth since it plunged blindly into industrialism, of the hideous mutilation of the countryside, followed by its dereliction. Its effect upon man as the bearer of evolving consciousness has been even more devastating. It has broken his relationship with nature, his participation in seasonal celebrations which gave rhythm to his life and helped to calm, like the rocking of a child in the cradle, the pain and agitation of his intellectual life. This is no mere sentimentalism. Has not our sage and subtle Palinurus, an intellectual sufferer of the industrial age if ever there was one, written: 'The more I see of life the more I perceive that only through solitary communion with nature can one gain an idea of its richness and meaning. I know that in such contemplation lies my true personality.' For those less subtle the need is not for contemplation but participation in nature, the deep-seated memories of our unity with it which have expressed themselves in The Great Goddess, the Dying God, and many other of our loveliest, most satisfying myths. These images are within us, they have accumulated there for millions of years; when they are denied an outlet it is as terrible for a man as to be stricken dumb or blind.

Not only have ordinary men and women been denied this natural cradling and expression for the indwelling images of their unity with nature, but they (and more especially men) have lost the satisfaction of expressing it more humbly through the crafts in making things whose forms repeat this ancient harmony. I have been accused of failing to appreciate the beauty of such things as aeroplanes. This is not so, and I hope as they are perfected more machines will acquire grace of form. But these things have been constructed by the intellect in conformity with physical laws, as in this instance of the passing of a body at speed through air. Thus they possess the beauty of a seagull, a porpoise, or a piece of wind-shaped rock, and this is very great, but it can never satisfy the imaginative needs of the men who work machines to make them; nor can they possibly express the higher imaginative perceptions of man.

The work in which the greater part of an industrial population is employed must always be of the repetitive kind which rapidly becomes automatic. This means, in fact, that the tasks are taken over almost entirely by the motor centres of the brain, and the worker forfeits the exercise of the whole brain in thought, imagination, sensibility, and skill which went with individual craftsmanship. Presumably this loss must stunt the growth of mind.

However, the consequences of industrialism with

which I am more concerned in thinking of our life in the physical world, are two of quite a different kind. First, the astronomical increase in the number of men on earth. Second, the frantically excessive production of material objects and man's inevitable preoccupation with both manufacturing and using them. Science has added a development which makes an alarming combination with these other two—the binding together of vast populations by means of mass communications.

An enormous part of the energy and ingenuity of industrial activity (I will not call it either life or civilization) goes into making it possible for more human beings to be alive at one time. This is entirely disadvantageous, and promises in time to become catastrophic. One might think that two thousand five hundred million brains would serve the cause of consciousness better than a few hundred million. But this is not true; small populations put out as many flowers of imaginative or intellectual genius as do large, and often very many more. How wonderful if it were otherwise, and the New Elizabethan Age in Britain with its fifty-five million brains could give us ten times as much poetry, drama, philosophy, song as the five million of the old Elizabethans!

Great numbers are a positive evil in the morality of consciousness. The need to put roofs over their heads ruins natural beauty, and makes towns so huge as to become in large part destructive of civilized living instead of its very heart and essence. History has by now had time to prove that moderately sized, nonindustrial cities, where writers, poets, painters, philosophers, statesmen, foreign visitors, and wealthy dilettanti habitually meet and mingle, dropping in on one another, meeting casually in public and in eating and drinking places, make the finest of all hotbeds for producing the prize blooms of consciousness. With modern cities, where millions live in utter social incoherence, it is quite otherwise. The longing to escape from them, coupled with the ridiculous separation of man from his work, leads to slaughter, stench, further corruption of natural beauty and a most hideous waste of a great part of the spare time which industry claims to have won for us. Better an hour free from working for a living spent in peace and pleasure, than four hours, more than half of them spent in the oppression of crowded travel.

If the effect of numbers on the surroundings and conditions of our lives is bad, their effect on social freedom is yet more evil. Great numbers, unless they are subsistence-or-famine peasants, demand control. They are in danger like passengers in an overloaded boat, and must be shepherded, planned for, and always of necessity handled in vast groups with their impersonal, clumsy relationships. Many people who would like to fight for a reasonable anarchism are fearful to venture for fear it might lead to stampede or breakdown among the enormous urban populations where no one is able to keep himself alive if trade or services fail. Once the excuse for heavy-handed government is there then it is seized, exaggerated, turned to a mild or cruel tyranny.

So now we feel fearful that urban masses, strongly controlled, flattered by passive amusements, conditioned to the impersonal, machine-dominated and unimaginative slavery of industrial life may bring human existence ever closer to that of the social insects. An inane expectation is abroad of being governed into happiness. There seems more than a possibility of the weakening of individual mind and personality leading to a disastrous impoverishment of experience and lowering of consciousness. Already in America methods are being adopted in the name of efficiency and industrial psychology which seem intended to eliminate individuality and the troublesome rebellion and idiosyncrasy of true humanity. In Russia we know how far brainwashing and death are used to destroy those values to which our whole evolution has tended.

Let even those of us who seek social organization for what seem ideal ends remember that the State is an evil myth, projected by man when he loses faith in an established god. In such organization we shall never surpass the bees and termites whose societies we hold in no very high esteem. Let us agree, too, that while each society must strive to maintain equality in justice and in opportunity for rising to the fullness of human life, the pursuit of equality for its own sake has no virtue and much evil. In an organic society the few who have won privilege belong to the many who have granted it, as the fruits belong to the living tree.

It is interesting to compare the communism of a Sumerian city state with the Soviet system. In the ancient form every citizen had to work part of the time on the estates of the god; every craftsman had to make his contribution. Then for festivals and in times of need of custom the god's stewards opened their heaped granaries and crowded warehouses and made distributions to the people. It was a grave restriction of freedom, but individuals had their own fields and workshops and suffered no political interference in their own lives. The difference from the point of view of the morality of consciousness is immense, for whereas the privileged individual, be he priest or secular estate owner, who is dependent on land, rents, services, and traditional sanctions, may be idle, useless or worse, he may equally well cultivate the higher faculties of man, support artists and thinkers of all kinds and call out their powers through appreciation and opportunity. It is perfectly certain that the politically privileged, the ruling bosses of large urban populations, will be interested in power alone. Intellect, imagination can no more spring from naked power than roses from a guillotine.

For me this destruction of beauty, quiet, grace, and tranquillity and the provocation of over-government are far more serious evils resulting from planetary overcrowding than the danger of world famine which alone arouses public anxiety. A world with five thousand million inhabitants, which is a possibility at the present rate within this century, would surely be so abominable as to make starvation almost welcome. Yet I admit famine is a terrible enough prospect, and those who complacently say all is well because the marvels of science will produce food from deserts and oceans, belong to that horrid species the scientific Romantic. For although probably it is true we could by most wearisome toil extract more food from the earth, saying all is well effectively prevents anyone from attempting it on the scale demanded by the situation. A few violent gestures from an already outraged nature, and famine may strike suddenly. Fewer men on earth is in every way desirable. Why sweat to support more? The two great powers who oppose the control of our appalling fecundity make an odd pair:

the Communists and the Roman Catholics. Both have one aim in common, to win the power of sheer numbers, but the Catholics add their own distinctive twist. Recently the Pope reaffirmed his Church's disapproval of sexual enjoyment even in wedlock. A world overcrowded with human beings begotten without the bodily delight which has been granted to us? Truly the human mind is incalculable. I regard this deliberate policy on the part of both powers to be among the most dangerous and evil of our time.

Too many people; and these people, in many parts of the world, overwhelmed by far too many objects. While a vast amount of industrial energy is expended merely in making it possible to keep far too large a population fed, clothed, vetted, and housed after a fashion, there is, of course, some considerable margin to spare. This margin is expended on war and on material objects. From the birth of civilization man has been in the habit of pouring his resources into warfare, so although industry and science have combined to take all the animal enjoyment and all the gorgeous bravura out of fighting, this is no new aberration of our species. What is new is the tremendous expenditure on unnecessary objects in which his active mind and his recent faith in material progress have involved Western man. Always before, and at every level of culture, if man had time left over beyond what was demanded for feeding himself and killing his enemies he used most of it in art, ritual ceremony, junketing, and the service of the gods—or in meditation. Tombs reaching up to pyramids, statues reaching up to colossi, temples of every conceivable shape and size reaching up to St. Peter's, Salisbury spire, and the temple of Amon at Carnac;

carnivals, potlatches or peaceful holy days, man gave his time, imagination, and thought to all these, but never before did he use them to fill his house with a thousand 'things'. Perhaps the Puritan belief that hard work, profits, and the suppression of delight were pleasing to god began it, but it was turned into an avalanche only by industrial machines. Even if our own greed and competitiveness are not enough to make us fall into this trap, we are dragged into it by merciless campaigns of advertisement, hammering at our senses and our weaknesses, sometimes even forcing physical entry into our houses and thrusting objects into our reluctant hands. Young children still usually have strength of mind to resist, ignoring elaborate toyshop confections for something simple enough for their imagination to turn into riches. But soon we succumb, and by the wedding-day we have capitulated. Gone the dancing, and the heroic feasting and drinking; the main business now is in buying, dispatching, and acknowledging many scores of articles man and wife would be far better without. Using and maintaining so many possessions is exhausting to almost everybody; when it comes to the creators and thinkers, the high priests of consciousness, how much less valuable are cars, vacuum-cleaners, recording-machines, filing-cabinets, automatic calendars than some reasonably devoted servants or a begging bowl.

I cannot help believing there may be something sinister and extra-human at work behind our insect-like increase in numbers and the development of mass communications between them. We are habituated now to the idea of repetition on increasing scales —to likening the structure of the atom to that of a planetary system. In biological evolution cells multiplied, came together, and were gradually brought into highly organized, co-ordinated and, finally, conscious organisms by means of the central nervous system. Cannot our brain's development of wireless and television and all the related means for extending sights and sounds beyond the individual body to the swarming social body, be a repetition of this on a larger scale? At present the difference appears to be considerable: the evolution of the central nervous system made high consciousness possible, while wireless and television appear to be making it impossible. The super-personal awareness which could come into being through mass communication, the kind one dimly perceives, for example, when a fighter squadron, a gleaming silver flock of rigid birds, takes off from Britain and whirls in some vast manoeuvre over half Europe, the pilot reduced to an intermediary between a central control point and a machine, is not at all of the kind I have been concerned with in this book, or which could form the touchstone of any system of values as I understand them.

Equally sinister, though more familiar, is the use of mass communications for the deliberate corruption of consciousness. Starting from the excusable falsifications of wartime propaganda this threat extends to the terrifying obscenity of double-talk in which both the perpetrators and the dupes must at last lose all power to distinguish what is from what is not. This evil desecration of mind, rendering men mental lepers unfit for their duty to apprehend the truth of the world so far as they are able, must rank as the greatest sin in the morality of consciousness.

It is those whose individual humanity has been

weakened by industrial life who are usually most vulnerable to attack by the new system. While people who enjoy the exercise of man's higher faculties and people who remain in close contact with nature seem equally able to resist, machine-minders and file-flickers and also, unfortunately, children, are drawn to the instruments of mass communication, and particularly towards the television screen, by a fascination such as one can imagine nerves had for the huddled cells a few hundred million years ago.

I must add in passing, I do not believe the original invention of the camera to have contributed to this threat; on the contrary, I see it as the one invention of science which has significantly extended our consciousness in any but purely intellectual fields. The ciné camera enables us to change our apprehension of time, stopping, speeding, or slowing it at will, and to convey meaning and feeling, metaphor and simile by visible symbols. A minor art, perhaps, but the only wholly new one achieved by modern man.

I have followed the first of my two lines of thought to the end, recognizing in scientific industrialism with its ruin of beauty and of the harmony between man and nature, its inflation of numbers of human beings causing individuality to weaken and government control to grow stronger, and finally with its perpetual flood of material objects, the main error of our recent life in the external world. Now I must pursue the second, looking into the internal world of the mind to see if the source of error can be found there.

Years ago, when I had thoughts of trying to express some part of the theme of this book in poetic form, I intended to use the image of human history as a contention between light and darkness. Light was to represent first simple consciousness, then intellectual reason; darkness the unconscious mind and all the realm of bodily life and thoughtless nature in which it is rooted. As a subsidiary metaphor I might have used the opening up of a new land, with pioneers slowly felling the trees of unbroken primeval forests, letting in light where flowers and crops could grow. For the greater part of our history I should have shown light on the side of the good, that is to say of heightened consciousness and its values. But then as intellect waxed in power and arrogance, scornfully destroying myths and the darkness in which much wisdom dwelt, committing incredible follies in trying to rationalize the irrational—as when St. Thomas Aquinas argued as to what would happen to cannibals at the Resurrection—then the good would have been revealed as moving towards the side of darkness, while evil stalked without in the glaring destructive light. Satan, in fact, was to cease to be the power of darkness and become the demon of light. I might have developed my metaphor by describing lands ruined by the total destruction of their forests and wild places.

This old scheme still expresses the essential meaning of what I want to say, but as, after all, I am writing in prose I must attempt to develop it a little more exactly.

The pure intellect, which we can identify for convenience with the last great product of evolution, the human Cerebrum, only shook itself free from mythopoetic thought and began to look at the world objectively less than three thousand years ago. Its activities were checked during the Dark Ages and the rise of Christianity, though theologians continually misapplied it in ways damaging to the living myth. Christianity, moreover, further endangered the future of consciousness by driving Greek dualism to a grim excess, and filling Western man with hatred of his body and especially of the plunge into the unconscious demanded by the sexual aspect of creative love.

When at the Renaissance the rational intellect leapt up with renewed strength, it hastened along the road on which the Ionian Greeks had been the first to set foot, the way which leads to the breaking down of the universe by observation and analysis in order to gain power over it and use it for human ends. This was the opposite to the chosen way of the great Athenians, who had generally preferred to fit nature to universal concepts. Man's pride in intellect mounted; myth, poetry, and all other imaginative and intuitive perception became no more than trifling ornaments to those in power. Soon he turned the new instrument, sharpened on his natural matrix, upon himself, analysing his society, his body, and his mind. Man's scientific approach to himself accomplished many most valuable things; medicine relieving us of the smaller agonies and tragedies of life; psychology making us more tolerant and a little wiser; sociology and economics perhaps reducing some few of the distresses caused by industrialization. But all these analytical sciences or would-be sciences have also done us damage. Medicine, least of all, though it has encouraged a wrong attitude to death, and has given us an insoluble problem in making it possible, and therefore a moral obligation, to prolong the lives of the very aged and sick to their own misery and the heavy burdening of the young. Freudian psychology, in strong contrast with that of Jung, has done great injury in spreading the idea that because in our inheritance from the wilderness some apparently disagreeable and primitive urges are included, these are in some way more 'true' and significant than the higher aspects of our humanity. Economics and sociology have harmed us in making us think far too much about elementary functions of our society of which we used to be as unconscious as a healthy man of the working of his bowels—a tendency which ends in such neurotic obsessions as the Marxist conviction that all human history has been determined by economic forces. It has also led to much misspending of public funds; better, surely, to endow a good school than a Department of Education.

Analysis has brought us many boons, but we have been too ready to forget the greater value of the wholes which it destroys. I cannot convey this better in my own words than by quoting a verse of mine.

My loved one's face is cratered like the moon;
The moon, revealed, has lost the crown of night;
Who now can carve Orion from the stars,
Stretch the four-pointed swan in wheeling flight?
Snuff out your tapers, ancient Pleiades
You seven are seven no more but empty light,
Fade fast Andromeda and Cassiopeia—
From too close looking follows loss of sight.
My loved one's face is cratered like the moon,
Throneless, untenanted, the lands of night.

Yet probably we should have been glad to sacrifice these wider perceptions and all the riches of the unconscious if only the intellect had been able to impose its rule, reigning supreme as the last and highest creation of evolution over a world reduced to sweet reasonableness. But even this rather horrid success has been utterly denied. Like the most terrible of volcanic upheavals the neglected and unsatisfied depths of our psyche have erupted in cruelty and chaos, in the evil madness behind the atom bomb. There is, indeed, a grim propriety in the likelihood that so much analysis, such a breaking down of our world in order to win mastery over it, may end in the atomization of ourselves and our planet. When I see a shower of meteors I wonder whether it is the work of analytical thinkers who somewhere in the empyrean have succeeded in exploding the globe on which they lived.

Our condition can be viewed again in terms of the physical instrument of mind. Every message from the senses, every control of the bodily organs must reach the Cerebrum through the ancient animal brain with its charge of ancient memory patterns and emotions, its possible access to cosmic secrets. When overflattered at the expense of the emotional centres and the unconscious mind, the cerebral intellect develops the silliness to which it is prone, while the neglected depths, denied outlets through the harmonious working of the whole psyche, may suddenly surge up in a violent and corrupted form. Cut off from one another, the mind's light and darkness both alike degenerate.

While we men of the West were active and curious, achieving wonders and finally hurling ourselves into the present predicament, eastern thinkers and mystics had learnt the mastery of the psyche, the balance of mental powers, of light and darkness. Now we are waking to our need of their wisdom, even while they seize, rather blindly perhaps, at the fruits of our activity. It is easier for the East to make good its failure to control the exterior world than it is for us to learn the ways of the psyche. Nor, of course, must we try to ape the Eastern methods and ideals, only be humble enough to learn from them. The West cannot forsake its own active ideal.

We have the benefits as well as the troubles of our intellectual thrust and curiosity. The very curiosity we took with us to Palestine has, in exposing the bare facts of our evolution, suggested our duty as the bearers of consciousness. Let this, then, be our accepted myth. Now as always it is true that nothing can be achieved except by the individual great or small. Nor need he rush out to break incautious lances in desperate sallies for reform. We can serve the myth by learning to experience the inner life, discovering what we can of the kingdom of heaven to which all have access. Many might begin just by staying at home.

We all have to find our own right balance of the mind, of activity, creativeness, or quiet, but at least we now know that we have need to harmonize light and darkness and that the delights and perceptions of the body and its senses flowing up into consciousness through their million nerves are a necessary part of its nourishment

If we can remain true to ourselves, the moment is coming when the powers of mind, which first cut us off from the animal's innocent communion with nature, will reunite us with it in conscious participation. We have discovered our past, identified the material ingredients of our bodies, and know that we have risen from slime through animality and still carry our history within us. We recognize that on earth, as we apprehend it, we live our lives without supernatural intervention. Yet we can hope that the very thoughts which tell us these things are a part of our approach to higher levels of being.

I have spoken of the modern artists' loss of faith in the nobility of man; perhaps the work of Henry Moore and others expresses instead this new sense of unity, and of kinship with the earth. From the ground they have prepared, a fresh expression of the greatness of our kind may spring with all the suddenness of art. If it dies it will be humbler than the old one, and free from the hypocrisy and sentimentality against which modern art has protested.

Once when I was a little crazy from grief I found myself drawing a symbol which may perhaps have expressed one aspect at least of the myth of the heightening of consciousness. The main device was an oak tree, rooted in the earth and with the sun above its crest each oval acorn of the tree held a human being, crouched embryo-like, and the whole was enclosed in an oval which was both an acorn and a human skull. Not perhaps a very appealing symbol, but one which for me, if I think of it together with my vision on Carmel of the caravan beneath the moon, does seem to help me towards my own apprehensions.

I am finishing this book in the month of May in open country in the south of England. The house is on a hilltop with chalk downs close behind, and looks out over a steep, wild slope across fields to the sea. From my window I have been able to watch white butterflies rising and falling idly above the bluebells, and beyond them white gulls tossing above the ploughland, or forming into a palpitating train behind the plough. In the fields of spring corn the last patches of red-brown soil have just been hidden beneath the spreading green.

I enjoy the perfection of each moment of these blue days, from the milky, shimmering mornings to sunset when the disc of Aten, now crimson red, sinks in palpable divinity behind the cliffs, and the flowers in the garden burn unnaturally bright. Yet I cannot help thinking with renewed wonder how this luscious young spring has taken a thousand million years and more to attain its present singing youth, having been conceived in a dead, hoary world and passed through an old age of flowerless evergreen. Great have been the powers of Eros, the Great Goddess, and the Dying God! If this natural spring can run counter to what seems to us the inevitable order of growing old in time, must there not be some counterpart in our own mental life, the psyche growing more fresh and resilient, more burgeoning, with the chain of individual lives an deaths?

While out of doors I am reminded of the perpetual renewing of the seasons, here in my room I have books, a few pictures, and some favourite possessions drawn from many ages and lands to remind me of the enduring treasures that mount from generation to generation. Surely we shall not betray so much promise, so much wealth, in self-destruction or in the deliberate or heedless betrayal of consciousness?

As a woman I suppose at heart I am confident in the goodness of existence and the need for it to go on. Our individual lives are of their very nature tragic, yet mind and senses together have grown up out of the darkness to equip us for delight. To be stretched between these two poles is the best exercise of the psyche. For the rest we can but look our ignorance in the face, for it is one of our few certainties. No religion, no philosophical or scientific system claiming any absolute or exclusive knowledge of truth is proper to our condition as inmates of one speck in a universe the vastness and wonder of which even our trifling minds are beginning faintly to apprehend.

It is because I accept our inevitable ignorance and the room within it for every kind of experience that I have dared to attempt this book, setting down my own vision of our lot, and affirming my faith in human life—and my love of it. We have much more to do yet to forward the springing of the psyche and must find the necessary laziness, energy, and discipline. It is our business on earth.

appendix

geological time-scale

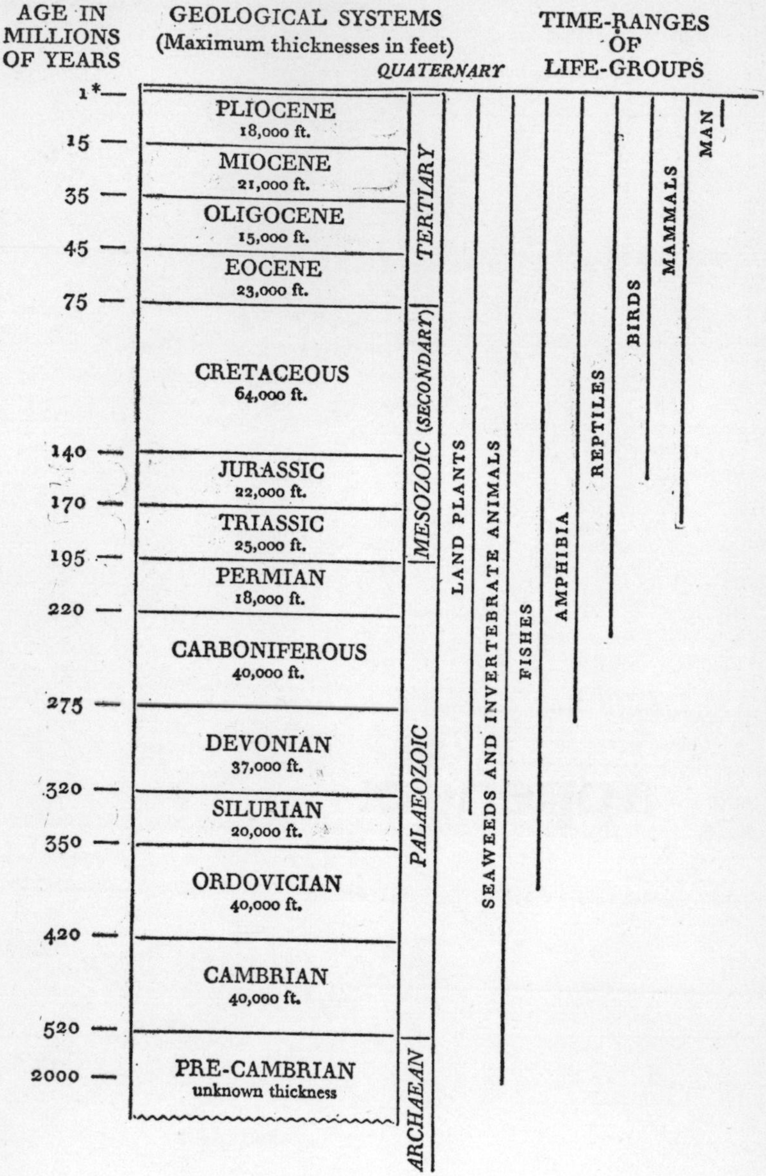

AGE IN MILLIONS OF YEARS	GEOLOGICAL SYSTEMS (Maximum thicknesses in feet)	
1*	QUATERNARY	
	PLIOCENE 18,000 ft.	TERTIARY
15		
	MIOCENE 21,000 ft.	
35		
	OLIGOCENE 15,000 ft.	
45		
	EOCENE 23,000 ft.	
75		
	CRETACEOUS 64,000 ft.	MESOZOIC (SECONDARY)
140		
	JURASSIC 22,000 ft.	
170		
	TRIASSIC 25,000 ft.	
195		
	PERMIAN 18,000 ft.	PALAEOZOIC
220		
	CARBONIFEROUS 40,000 ft.	
275		
	DEVONIAN 37,000 ft.	
320		
	SILURIAN 20,000 ft.	
350		
	ORDOVICIAN 40,000 ft.	
420		
	CAMBRIAN 40,000 ft.	
520		
2000	PRE-CAMBRIAN unknown thickness	ARCHAEAN

TIME-RANGES OF LIFE-GROUPS

LAND PLANTS

SEAWEEDS AND INVERTEBRATE ANIMALS

FISHES

AMPHIBIA

REPTILES

BIRDS

MAMMALS

MAN

* *Quaternary (Pleistocene and Holocene) 4,000 feet*

man's genealogy

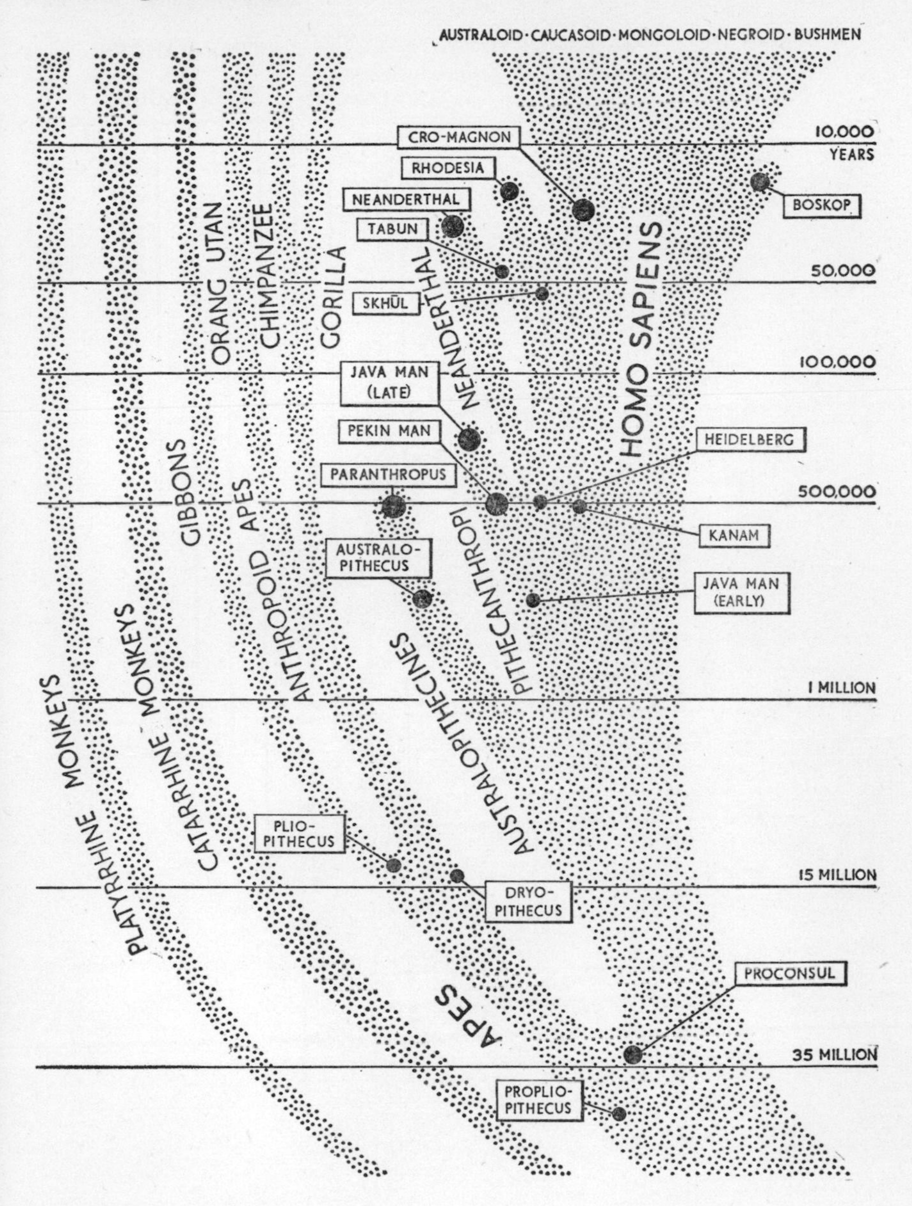

Based on material provided by Dr. Kenneth Oakley of the British Museum of Natural History

index

A Land, and industrialism, 213
AGGRESSION, 37-8
AKHENATEN, 187-89, 190
AKHETATEN, *see* Amarna, el
ALCOHOL, 143, 144
ALEXANDER, 196
ALEXANDRIA, 197
ALPHABET, the, 6; phonetic, 193
ALPHA-RHYTHM, the, 127, 128, 129
ALTAMIRA, 98
AMARNA, EL, 162, 188, 189, 191
AMENHOTEP IV, *see* Akhenaten
AMMONITES, 20
AMOEBA, 28
AMON, 188
AMPHIBIANS, 24, 41, 45
ANALYTICAL THOUGHT, 225
ANAXIMANDER, 194
ANCIENT WORLD, end of, 191-92
ANIMALS, domestic, 59
ANIMALS, domestication of, 140
ANNING, MARY, 54
APES, 24, 61; man's relationship to, 63-4; Dryopithecus, 66; Parapithecus, 66; Pliopithecus, 66; Proconsul, 66; Propliopithecus, 66; their use of implements, 74-5
AQUINAS, ST. THOMAS, 223
ARABS, the, 206
ARCHETYPES, 123
ARCHETYPES, and religion, 167
ARGUS PHEASANT, 18, 22, 52
ARISTARCHUS, 199, 212
ARISTOTLE, 103, 105, 199
ART, beginnings of, 81, 97-8; modern, 210
ASTRONOMY, 198-99

ATEN, 188
ATHENIANS, 224
ATHENS, 199
AUSTRALOPITHECUS, 67-8, 70, 85; speech of, 95
AZTECS, 169

BABYLON, 172
BABYLONIANS, 189
BACKBONE, 33, 34, 38, 41, 44, 47
BACON, FRANCIS, 5
BERLIN, 191
BIRDS, 58
BIRDS, brain of, 110
BLAKE, WILLIAM, 138
BLOOD, warm, 49
BRAIN, 22, 44, 102, 104-133, 137; developed by sight and touch, 47; and warm blood, 49; of Australopithecus, 69; of Pithecanthropus, 72; of Neanderthal Man, 87; old, 226
BRAINS, mechanical, 108
BRITISH MUSEUM, The, 150
BUDDHA, 192, 194

CAENOZOIC ERA, 57, 58, 60, 61
CALCULATING BOY, The, 116
CAMBRIAN AGE, 29, 31, 32, 33, 36, 49
CARBONIFEROUS AGE, 41
CARLYLE, 105
CARMEL, MOUNT, 3, 4, 6, 23, 140, 228
CARNIVORES, men become partial, 69
CATHOLICS, ROMAN, 219
CELTS, the, 203
CEREALS, cultivation of, 140
CEREBELLUM, 107, 110
CEREBRUM, the, 107, 110, 111, 112, 113, 114, 116, 117, 118, 119, 124, 125, 132, 176, 196, 223, 226
CHILD-BEARING, 11
CHILDE, GORDON, 175
CHIMPANZEES, 64
CHINA, 195
CHORDATES, the, 32
CHOUKOUTIEN CAVES, 75, 85
CHRISTIANITY, 190, 201, 202, 203, 204, 205, 223, 224
CHRISTIANITY and erotic love, 121
CHURCHILL, SIR WINSTON, 12
CINEMA, the, 222
CITIES, the earliest, 153, 154; ancient, 162; modern, 216
CIVILIZATION, and the unconscious mind, 135
CIVILIZATION, its fragility, 136-7; beginning of, in the river valleys, 157; in Mesopotamia, 161; in Egypt and Mesopotamia compared, 164; pre-Columban, 169; spread of, 172; rise and fall of, 177; variety within a single, 178
COELACANTHS, 40
COINAGE, invention of, 193
COLLECTIVE UNCONSCIOUS, the, and brain, 122
COLORADO, river, 27
COLUMBUS, 206
COMMUNISM, 217
COMMUNISTS, 219
CONFUCIUS, 192, 194
CONQUISTADORS, the, 169
CONSCIOUSNESS, 6, 7, 8, 10, 13, 18, 33, 44, 50, 56, 105, 134, 168, 192; and writing, 156; and city life, 171; morality of, 209, 215, 218, 221; corruption of, 221; heightening of, 130; myth of, 227
COOKING, beginning of, 69
COPERNICUS, 206, 212
CORALS, 35, 36
CORPORA QUADRIGEMINA, 107, 110
CORTES, 170
CORTEX, *see* Cerebrum
COWS, their small size, 39
CRETACEOUS AGE, 51, 55
CRO-MAGNON MAN, 91, 92, 97
CROSSOPTERYGII, 40
CULTURE, and evolution, 22; of Australopithecus, 68, 69; of

Pithecanthropus, 74; conservatism of, 80; and imagination, 176
CURIOSITY, scientific, 5, 7

DEATH, man's encounter with, 182
DESCARTES, 109, 130
DESCENT, of man, 24
DEVONIAN AGE, 36, 38, 41
Dialogue of Pessimism, 184, 185
DIFFUSE RETICULAR SYSTEM, 112
DINCHTHYS, 39
DINOSAURS, 20, 51, 52, 54, 56
DIPLODOCUS, 53
DISASTERS, in human history, 211
DOMESTIC ANIMALS, 59
DOUBLE-TALK, 221
DUALISM, 201, 224, 226
DYING GOD, the, 167, 214, 229

EARTH, exploration of, 198, 206
EAST AND WEST, divergence of, 196; convergence of, 226
ECONOMICS, 225
EGYPT, early civilization in, 157; unification of, 158; static ideal of, 160
ELIZABETH, QUEEN, of England, 33
EMOTIONS, of men and animals, 47
ENGELS, 150
ENLIL, 161
EOCENE AGE, 58, 59, 62
EQUESTRIAN STATUES, 176
ERECH, 162, 168
ERIDU, 162
EROS, 8, 10, 14, 15, 17, 29, 229
ERYOPS, 41
EVOLUTION, 17, 18, 22-3
EXPERIENCE, of men and animals, 46; creative, importance of, 209
EYE, reptilian, 47

FAMINE, 218
FARMING, beginning of, 139; psychological significance, 141
FEMININE PRINCIPLE, the, 149, 168, 196
FIRES, early use by man, 75
FISHES, 24, 58; the earliest, 36; ascendancy of in Devonian Age, 38; carnivorous, 39; leave the water, 40
FLINTS, 6
FORESTS, carboniferous, 36, 43
FOSSILS, 25, 32, 39
FREUD, 224
FUTURE, sense of, 78

GALILEO, 212
GENIUS, 21 24, 96, 97, 209, 215
GILGAMESH, Epic of, 180, 181, 182
GILL POUCHES, in human foetus, 13
GLACIATION, Pleistocene, 77
GODS, creation of, 154, 166
GOTHIC ARCHITECTURE, 213
GRAND CANYON, 27, 33
GRAPTOLITES, 35
GREAT GODDESS, the, 101, 125, 148-9, 167, 214, 229
GREAT MOTHER, The, 198
GREAT WALL, of China, 196
GREEK, intellect, 173
GREEKS, Ionian, 192, 194, 199, 212, 224; The, and the beginning of science, 197; Hellenistic, 197, 199, 212
GULLIVER, voyages of, 59

HAMMURABI, laws of, 179
HAND-AXE, history of, 79
HANDS, origins of, 42; use of, 62; of apes, 64; saved from overspecialization, 70
HATHOR, 148
HATSHEPSUT, QUEEN, 187
HEBREW PROPHETS, The, 192
HEBREWS, The, 189, 202
HEIDELBERG MAN, 71
HERACLEITUS, 194
HERETICS, the, 212
HISTORY, two points of view, 173
HOMER, 177

HOMO SAPIENS, final victory of, 88
HORSES, their small size, 39
HORSETAILS, 36
HORUS, 159
HUMMING-BIRD, 21, 22
HUXLEY, ALDOUS, 145

IMPLEMENTS, 6
INCAS, 169
INDIVIDUALITY, consciousness of, 186; weakening of, 217
INDUSTRIALISM, 212, 214
INSECTS, 48, 58
INSTINCT, 45, 73, 138
INTELLECT, growth of, 172; sudden awakening of, 192; comes into its own, 200; the, 223
INTOXICATION, 143, 144
INVERTEBRATES, 29
ISHTAR, 149
ISIS, 159, 188

JAMOYTIUS, 34, 38
JAVA MAN, 71
JELLY-FISH, 27, 33
JERICHO, 152
JUNG, 123, 224
JURASSIC AGE, 51, 55

KISH, 162

LAGASH, 162
LANCELETS, 34
L'ANGLE-SUR-L'ANGLIN, Old Stone Age art at, 60, 98; portrait of a man from, 101
LANGUAGE, first development of, 95
LAO-TSZE, 192, 194
LASCAUX, 98, 177
LAWRENCE, D. H., 111
LEMURS, 61
LEONARDO DA VINCI, 177, 206
LIFE, arboreal, 22, 62; beginning of, 25; continuity of, 32, 46; comes on land, 43; its unity, 73
LIGHT AND DARKNESS, contention between, 222
LINNAEUS, 61
LOVE, creative, 10; and sexual passion, 14
LYME REGIS, 54

MALTA, 149
MAMMALS, the, 42, 50, 52; their development delayed, 50; Triassic, 50; Age of, 56, 59
MARDUK, 161, 183
MASCULINE PRINCIPLE, the, 150
MASS COMMUNICATIONS, 220, 221
MATERIAL OBJECTS, excess of, 219
MATHEMATICS, beginning of, 155
MEDULLA, 107, 109, 110
MEDUSAS, *see* Jelly-fish
MEMORY, 45, 118
MEMPHIS, 162, 172
MIDDLE STONE AGE, 139, 145
MIND, 105, 126, 130
MIND AND CULTURE, 132
MIND RHYTHMS, electric in brain, 126
MIOCENE AGE, 58, 64, 65
MOLLUSCS, 31
MONKEYS, 61, 63
MONOTHEISM, 189
MONTEZUMA, 169
MORALITY, 209
MOZART, 21, 24
MYELIN, 113
MYTHS, of creation, 25, 26, 27; Sumerian, 161

NATURAL HISTORY MUSEUM, 18
NATURAL SELECTION, 17, 19
NEANDERTHAL MAN, 71, 86, 87; his ritual life, 88; extinction of, 90
NEFERTITI, QUEEN, 188, 191
NERVE CELLS, 104, 126
NERVE, CENTRAL, 33
NERVOUS SYSTEM, CENTRAL, 34, 44, 107, 221
NEW STONE AGE, domestic life in, 151; religious cults of, 148

NEW WORLD, civilization in the, 169, 203
NEWTON, 212
NILE VALLEY, the, 158
NOTOCHORD, 34

OLD KINGDOM, of Egypt, 158, 161
OLD STONE AGE, the, 77, 92; later, 89; sudden progress towards end of, 90; art of the, 97, 99; ritual in the, 99
OLIGOCENE AGE, 58, 62
ORDOVICIAN AGE, 35, 36
OSIRIS, 159, 188
OSTRACODERMS, 37, 38
OVERCROWDING, of planet, 216, 218
OXYGEN, 36, 40

PALINURUS, 213
PARAMECIUM, 28
PAUL, ST., 202
PAVLOV, 138
PEKIN MAN, 71, 78
PERMIAN AGE, 47, 48
PHARAOH, 158, 164, 188; divinity of, 159
PHILOSOPHY, 200
PHOENICIANS, 193
PIGS, giant, 59
PINEAL EYE, 109, 130
PITHECANTHROPUS, 67, 70, 71, 72, 74, 85, 114; speech of, 95
PLATO, 199, 201
PLEISTOCENE AGE, 60, 76, 78, 84
PLIOCENE AGE, 58
PLOUGH, the, 174
PONS, 107, 110
POPE, The, 219
POTTING, beginning of, 146
PRE-CAMBRIAN AGE, 27, 28, 31
PRE-FRONTAL LOBOTOMY, 119
PRIESTS, intellectual adventures of, 155
PRIMATES, 59, 61; early, 61
PROGRESS, idea of, 208, 210
PROMETHEUS, 209
PROUST, 177, 201
PSYCHE, 15; the, 166, 196, 202, 205, 226, 227
PSYCHOLOGY AND BRAIN, 122
PTERODACTYLS, 52
PYRAMIDS, 22, 154, 168
PYTHAGORAS, 192, 195

RACES OF MAN, beginnings of, 92
RENAISSANCE, The, 206, 210, 224
REPTILES, 24, 50, 51, 55; mammal-like, 49; Age of, 50
RHODESIAN MAN, 71, 91
RHYTHMS, electric, in brain, 126
RIGHT-HANDEDNESS, 115
'RIGHTS OF MAN,' 184
ROMANS, The, 203
ROMANTIC MOVEMENT, the, 212
RUSSIA, 217

SAIL, the, 174
SATAN, 223
SCOLOSAURUS, 53
SEA-CUCUMBERS, 30, 31, 32, 38
SEA-URCHINS, 30, 31
SEMITES, 164, 178
SENSES, sharpening of, 47
SEX, beginning of, 28, 29; enjoyment of, 219
SEX MORALITY, beginnings of, 89; and culture, 90
SHERRINGTON, SIR CHARLES, 103, 127
SIGHT, beginning of, 31
SILURIAN AGE, 35, 36, 37
SIXTH CENTURY B.C., the, 193
SKULL, 7, 102; of Neanderthal Man, 87
SLEEP, 128
SOCIOLOGY, 225
SOCRATES, 144, 192
SOUTH AFRICA, evolution of apes in, 65
SPENGLER, 174
SPONGES, 35
STATE, the, 217
STEGOSAURUS, 53
STONESFIELD LIMESTONE, 51

SUMERIANS, the, 161, 162, 163, 165, 178
SWANSCOMBE MAN, 82, 83, 84, 85
SYLVIAN FISSURE, 117

TADPOLE, 41
TARSIERS, 61
TEMPLES, Sumerian, 154
THALAMUS, 107, 111, 112, 113, 120, 121, 123, 125, 132
THEBES, 162, 172, 188
THEOLOGY, 200
THYROID GLAND, 105
TIME, and eternity, 7, 23; linear, 23
TITANICHTHYS, 39, 46
TOOLS, of Pithecanthropus, 74; the first stereotyped, 78; the earliest, 79, 85; of Neanderthal Man, 87
TOPOSCOPE, 126
TORTOISES, 8, 20
TOSCANINI, 33
TOYNBEE, 174, 192
TRAPS, first use of, 78
TREE-CLIMBING, atavistic, 62
TREES, DECIDUOUS, the earliest, 56
TREE-SHREWS, 24
TRIASSIC AGE, 47, 48, 50
TRILOBITES, 30, 50
TYRANNOSAURUS, 37, 46, 53, 54

UNCONSCIOUS, memory of forms in the, 81; the, 137
UNCONSCIOUS MIND, inherited memories of the, 137; the, 144, 167, 176
UR, 162, 172, 186

VEGETATION, appears on land, 36; deciduous, 55
VERTEBRAE, *see* Backbone
VERTEBRAL COLUMN, *see* Backbone
VERTEBRATES, 38, 40, 47
VILLAGE MAYOR, The, Old Kingdom sculpture, 161
VILLAGES, the earliest, 146, 152; spread of, 151
VIRUS, the, 26

WEAVER BIRD, 72, 78, 137
WEAVING, beginning of, 147
WHEEL, the, 174
WILL OF GOD, myth of the, 202
WOMAN, and natural process, 12; in the New Stone Age, 146, 147
WOODPECKERS, 20
WRITING, invention of, 156

XENOPHANES, 194

YAHWEH, 189

ABOUT THE AUTHOR

JACQUETTA HAWKES is the younger daughter of Sir Frederick Gowland Hopkins, O.M., who was a first cousin of the poet Gerard Manley Hopkins. She grew up at Cambridge and from an early age was determined to study archaeology, being drawn to it partly by a visual enjoyment of things and of styles, partly by a growing awareness of the poetry of history. She read archaeology and anthropology at Newnham College, Cambridge, and for a year afterwards had a research scholarship. She excavated at a number of sites in England and elsewhere and published papers in specialized journals and a monograph on the archaeology of Jersey. Early in the war she entered the War Cabinet Offices, later transferring to the Ministry of Education where she became British secretary to the British National Commission of UNESCO.

During this period she published *Prehistoric Britain* (jointly with Christopher Hawkes) and *Early Britain* in the "Britain in Pictures" series. She resigned from UNESCO and from the civil service in order to devote herself to writing, in which she found herself growing more and more absorbed for its own sake, and to research.

She is married to J. B. Priestley, the distinguished author, spending her winters in London and summers on the Isle of Wight.